J. M. McWilliams

Descriptive Statistics

DESCRIPTIVE
STATISTICS

Stanley S. Blank
UNIVERSITY OF BRITISH COLUMBIA

Appleton-Century-Crofts
NEW YORK | DIVISION OF MEREDITH CORPORATION

Acknowledgments

I am grateful to various colleagues who have spent much time reviewing, experimenting with, and most helpfully criticizing this manuscript. I must also extend my appreciation to the many students who used the text and made useful suggestions. Finally, I would like to express my deepest gratitude to my wife for her unstinting help and encouragement.

Preface

DESCRIPTIVE STATISTICS is an outgrowth of a very real need. Its purpose is to free instructors in introductory psychology, educational psychology, and introductory measurement and evaluation courses from the necessity of teaching basic descriptive statistics.

The text employs a programmed approach, a technique which has proven to be a particularly effective means of teaching many basic kinds of material. This is especially true for statistics. Experience and research in programmed instruction demonstrate that students can rapidly and effectively pursue this subject matter on their own.

This particular program has been developed over three years of trial and revision with some fifteen hundred freshman, sophomore, and junior university students enrolled in several different courses in psychology and educational psychology. It also has been used most effectively with some three hundred students in a basic measurement and evaluation course over the same three-year period.

The topical arrangement and scope of the program have evolved from students' comments on their experience with it, together with the author's experience in teaching statistics to psychology and education students. Most of the presently existing statistics texts, programmed or otherwise, pay only cursory attention to basic descriptive statistics; then they move on to more advanced concepts. For most students in basic psychology and educational psychology courses, however, it is the descriptive statistics that are of primary concern. For this reason DESCRIPTIVE STATISTICS limits itself to this area and is specifically designed to teach these topics: frequency distributions, measures of central value, measures of variability, standard scores, percentiles and correlations. The basic objective of this text is to teach the student how to calculate each of these statistics, on the assumption that such ability will carry with it additional facility in understanding the research literature. It leaves the concepts of inferential statistics to statistics courses proper.

The experience of a number of instructors with this final version of the text indicates that students are able to complete the program in an average of ten to twelve hours of independent study, and to master the concepts as thoroughly as those students taught by more conventional methods. The students themselves almost invariably have shown enthusiasm for the technique and organization of the program, and have expressed surprise at the rapidity with which they were able to master the topics presented in the text.

It is my earnest hope that this text will be as helpful to other instructors of psychology and education as it has been to my colleagues and me.

S.S.B.

Contents

Introduction

1 This text is designed in such a way that you must proceed through it one item or "frame" at a time. This is the first frame.

Each frame presents some new material you are to learn and, frequently asks a question on that material. First, turn to the last page of the book and cut out the answer mask. Place the mask flat on the page, and slide it down until the first heavy line is visible just above the top of the mask. Then, after you have read the frame and responded to the question, move the top of the mask down to the next heavy line in order to find the correct answer. Compare your answer with the one that is given.

After each answer you will find italicized instructions telling you which frame to study next. Each frame is numbered so it can be found easily.

Go on to frame 2.

2 This is the second item or frame in the program.

Sometimes, as was the case in the last frame, you will be required only to read through the frame and no response will be called for.

Go on to frame 3.

1

3 In those frames which require a response, the required response may be only a single word. If this is the case, the blank will look like this:

_____.

Example: The capital city of England is _____.

The answer, of course, is "London." Write London in the answer space.

London

Go on to frame 4.

4 If the required response to a question is two or more words, the blank will look like this:

_____ _____ (one blank for each missing word or symbol).

Example: The name of this book is

_____ _____.

The answer is "DESCRIPTIVE STATISTICS." Write the answer in the answer space.

DESCRIPTIVE STATISTICS

Go on to frame 5.

5 Sometimes the required answer to a question will be a number. In this case, the blank will look like this:

_____

Example: The largest number in the series 9, 12, 15, 18, 21 is _____.

The answer is "21." Write 21 in the answer space.

21

Go on to frame 6.

6 Should the answer to the question be a symbol, the blank will look like this: _____ .

Example: The symbol _____ always appears at the end of a sentence which asks a question.

The answer is " ?." Write the answer in the appropriate space.

?

Go on to frame 7.

7 Occasionally, you may be given several alternatives from which to choose your answer. Such choices will be preceded by letters. You are then to select the choice you think correct and write that alternative in the answer space.

Example: The capital city of the United States is:

(a) New York City (b) Washington, D.C. (c) Ottawa
(d) California

Write your answer and check it. _____

(Be sure to write your response in the answer space.)

(b) Washington, D.C.

If your answer is the same as the one above, go to frame 9.

If your answer is not the same as the one above, go on to frame 8.

8 New York City is in the United States but it is not the capital city. Ottawa is the capital city of Canada. California is a state, not a capital city.

The capital city of the United States then is

_____ .

Washington, D.C.

Go on to frame 9.

9 If the question asked requires you to compute an answer, do your calculations in the work space provided at the back of the book. After you have calculated your answer write it down in the answer space.

Go on to frame 10.

Rank Order

10 When we want to handle large numbers of people or things, we find that it is most economical and efficient to organize them into groups or categories.

One place where organization of large numbers of men is important is the army. In the army men are organized into groups such as squads, platoons, companies, and so on. This is done because it is the most efficient way to handle such large masses of men. As you can imagine, the purpose of the organization will determine the type of organization.

Go on to frame 11.

11 In manipulating large numbers of scores, the most efficient way of handling them is to organize them.

One of the ways to organize scores is to put them in order from highest to lowest, that is, to rank order the scores.

Example: The scores 15, 14, 12, 11, 9, 8, 4, 3 are arranged in rank order with score 15 ranked 1, score 14 ranked 2, score 12 ranked 3, and so on. Or we could rank score 3 as 1, score 4 would then be ranked 2, and so on, up to score 15 which would be ranked 8.

Go on to frame 12.

12 The scores 60, 59, 55, 40, 32, 30, 25 are arranged in

_____ _____.

Rank order

Go on to frame 13.

13 Arrange the following set of scores in rank order and assign ranks to them; that is, assign to these scores by plac-
ing above each score the numbers which indicate the order
in which they occur after being rank ordered. You may
order them from either end. (1, 2, 3, 4, 5, ... 8.)

20, 21, 19, 17, 18, 22, 16, 25.

---

  8   7   6   5   4   3   2   1
25, 22, 21, 20, 19, 18, 17, 16 or
  1   2   3   4   5   6   7   8

Go on to frame 14.

14   25, 23, 22, 19, 18, 18, 18, 17.

The rank order for the preceding set of scores is:

  1   2   3   4   6   6   6   8
25, 23, 22, 19, 18, 18, 18, 17 or
  8   7   6   5   3   3   3   1

Note that here since ranks 5, 6 and 7 are all occupied by
the score 18, we have no way of ranking one above the
other, and yet since score 17 is the eighth score, the 18's
must occupy ranks 5 through 7. Since they are equal, we
average the ranks 5, 6 and 7 and each score of 18 gets the
rank 6. Now since ranks 5, 6 and 7 have been used up, the
next available rank is 8, so score 17 gets the rank 8.

Similarly if we start with score 17 as rank 1 then the 18's

6

occupy ranks 2, 3 and 4. Averaging these we find that each score of 18 gets the rank 3.

Go on to frame 15.

15 Now arrange this set of scores in rank order and assign ranks to them. (You may rank them from either end.)

$$25, 24, 23, 23, 23, 21, 20, 19, 23.$$

Remember, when you average a set of scores you <u>add</u> the scores and divide by the number of scores.

```
 9    8   5.5  5.5  5.5  5.5   3    2    1
25,  24,  23,  23,  23,  23,  21,  20,  19 or
 1    2   4.5  4.5  4.5  4.5   7    8    9
```

Go on to frame 16.

16 Arrange the following set of scores in rank order and assign ranks to them:

$$27, 31, 33, 28, 28, 29, 35, 35, 35, 38.$$

```
 1    3    3    3    5    6    7   8.5  8.5  10
38,  35,  35,  35,  33,  31,  29,  28,  28,  27 or
10    6    6    6    6    5    4   2.5  2.5   1
```

If you answered correctly, proceed to frame 19.
If you did <u>not</u> answer correctly, go on to frame 17.

17 The rank order arrangement of the scores is:

38, 35, 35, 35, 33, 31, 29, 28, 28, 27.

Score 38 ranks 1. Therefore, score 35 must rank 2. But there are three scores of 35. So, because they all can't be second, they must occupy ranks 2, 3 and 4. Since we obviously have no basis for ranking one above the other, we assign each the average of these three ranks, or 3. Similarly, with the scores 28 and 28. They must occupy ranks 8 and 9 (why?), and we assign them the average of these two ranks, or 8.5. Score 27 is now given rank 10. (Why?)

The same reasoning applies if you started your ranking with score 27 ranked as 1.

Since 28 and 28 can't both occupy the eighth rank, they are said to occupy the eighth and ninth ranks which are then averaged to get the rank 8.5 for each score because it would make no sense to rank one above the other.

Thus, 27 is ranked 10 because the ranks 8 and 9 are already occupied by the scores 28 and 28.

Go on to frame 18.

18 Arrange the following set of scores in rank order and assign ranks to them:

15, 16, 14, 14, 14, 13, 18, 17, 17, 19, 20.

1	2	3	4.5	4.5	6	7	9	9	9	11
20,	19,	18,	17,	17,	16,	15,	14,	14,	14,	13 or
11	10	9	7.5	7.5	6	5	3	3	3	1

Go on to frame 19.

19 Now let's review what we've covered so far.

(a) One way of handling a set of scores most efficiently is to place them in (1) _____ _____.

(b) If, when we are assigning ranks to the scores, there are a number of tie scores, we assign these tie scores consecutive ranks, (2) _____ these ranks, and then assign this new average rank to all the tie scores.

---

(1) rank order
(2) average

Go on to frame 20.

---

20 Just in case you have forgotten, we are talking about how to handle large numbers of scores most efficiently.

So far we have discussed rank ordering scores as one way to efficiently handle scores. However, when we have large numbers of scores, rank ordering them is not the most efficient way to handle them. For example, if we had 1000 scores, rank-ordering them would be a difficult task.

Go on to frame 21.

Frequency Tables

21 Another, and even more efficient, way to handle large numbers of scores is to group them into ordered groups, or intervals.

For example, suppose we had given a spelling test to fifty grade school children and obtained the following scores:

20, 19, 15, 20, 22, 23, 25, 27, 26, 30, 31, 33, 34, 33, 35, 34, 33, 18, 50, 51, 42, 43, 39, 38, 40, 44, 45, 47, 46, 42, 49, 53, 19, 18, 16, 18, 29, 32, 40, 50, 52, 51, 42, 45, 40, 22, 24, 31, 50, 44.

We could rank order these scores (too inefficient) or we could put them into ordered groups (or intervals).

Go on to frame 22.

22 One way of grouping the scores would result in a table that looks like this:

Interval	Frequency
49–53	8
44–48	6
39–43	8
34–38	4
29–33	8
24–28	4
19–23	7
14–18	5

A table like this is known as a <u>frequency table</u> because it shows the groups and the frequency (or number) of scores within each group.

Go on to frame 23.

23 A table which shows the groupings of scores and the number of scores within each group is known as a

_____ _____.

Frequency table

Go on to frame 24.

24 A frequency table shows the intervals (or groups) into which scores have been divided and the
_____ of scores within each interval.

Frequency (number)

Go on to frame 25.

25 Now let's look at how you set up a frequency table.

Let's take the spelling test example again. We have these fifty scores:

20, 19, 15, 20, 22, 23, 25, 27, 26, 30, 31, 33, 34, 33, 35, 34, 33, 18, 50, 51, 42, 43, 39, 38, 40, 44, 45, 44, 47, 46, 42, 49, 53, 19, 18, 16, 18, 29, 32, 40, 50, 52, 51, 42, 45, 40, 22, 24, 31, 50.

Go on to frame 26.

RANGE

26 First, how do you decide how many intervals you will use?

By convention, we commonly use from 10 to 15 equal intervals (with no gaps between the intervals). Of course, the number of intervals will dictate how large the intervals will be.

The first step is to find the range of scores—that is, the difference between the lowest and highest scores. For example, the range of scores in our spelling test set of scores (frame 25) is _____ minus _____ or _____.

Look at this set of scores and find the range.

---

53 − 15 or 38

Go on to frame 27.

27 When setting up a frequency table, the first step is to find the (1) _____ of scores.

This is done by (2) _____ the (3) _____ from the (4) _____ score.

---

(1) range
(2) subtracting
(3) lowest
(4) highest

Go on to frame 28.

28 Find the range of the following set of scores:

26, 23, 23, 18, 18, 17, 16, 15, 14, 10, 10, 9, 8.

The range is 26 − 8 = 18.

Go on to frame 29.

INTERVAL SIZE

29 By convention, the optimal number of intervals is taken to be from (1) _____ to (2) _____ .

Find the range of the following set of scores. Pick the number of intervals you would prefer and state the resulting interval size.

52, 51, 49, 49, 49, 45, 44, 40, 39, 37, 37, 36, 35, 33, 33, 30, 29, 27, 26, 26, 22, 21, 20, 20, 19, 19, 19, 15, 14, 12, 12.

---

(1) 10
(2) 15

Go on to frame 30.

30 The range of scores in frame 29 is $52 - 12$ or 40.

If you chose 10 as your number of intervals the interval size would be $40 \div 10$ or 4.

If you chose 11 the interval size would be $40 \div 11$ or 3.6. But because we use only <u>whole numbers</u> for the interval size, we round <u>up</u> if the fraction is $\frac{1}{2}$ or over and <u>down</u> if it is less than $\frac{1}{2}$. Therefore, for 11 intervals the interval size is 4.

For 12, the interval size would be (1) _____ .
For 13, the interval size would be (2) _____ .
For 14, the interval size would be (3) _____ .
For 15, the interval size would be (4) _____ .

---

(1) 3 (3.3 rounded off to nearest whole number)
(2) 3 (3.1 rounded off to nearest whole number)
(3) 3 (2.9 rounded off to nearest whole number)
(4) 3 (2.7 rounded off to nearest whole number)

Go on to frame 31.

13

31 After you determine the number of intervals and the resulting interval size, the next step is to set up the intervals.

For example, consider the scores: 32, 30, 25, 25, 23, 21, 20, 20, 19, 18, 18, 17, 16, 16, 16, 15, 14, 12, 11, 11, 10, 10, 10, 9, 8, 7, 7, 6, 5, 5.

The range is 25 and, since we will choose 10 as our number of intervals, the interval size is 2.5 or 3.

Now, since our lowest score is 5, the bottom interval must include 5, so let's begin with the interval: 4–6 (4–5–6). (This is what is meant by interval size of 3.)

Next will be: 7– 9 (Note: We could have started with 5
             10–12   and then our bottom interval
             13–15   would have been 5–6–7. In
             16–18   other words, we can start with
             19–21   whatever interval we like so
             22–24   long as it <u>includes</u> the lowest
             25–27   score and ends with any in-
             28–30   terval that <u>includes</u> the high-
             31–33   est score.)

These intervals will take care of all our scores since our lowest score is 5 and the highest is 32.

Go on to frame 32.

FREQUENCY

32 Now that we have established our intervals, we can go on to the next step. This step involves finding out how many scores there are in each interval. To do this we put a tally (or count) mark beside the interval for each score in the interval.

The scores were: 32, 30, 25, 25, 23, 21, 20, 20, 19, 18, 18, 17, 16, 16, 16, 15, 14, 12, 11, 11, 10, 10, 10, 9, 8, 7, 7, 6, 5, 5.

The intervals were:

Interval	Tally	Now that we	Interval	Tally	Frequency
4– 6	///	have set up	4– 6	///	3
7– 9	////	our intervals	7– 9	////	4
10–12	//////	and tallied	10–12	//////	6
13–15	//	our scores,	13–15	//	2
16–18	//////	our next step	16–18	//////	6
19–21	////	is to indicate	19–21	////	4
22–24	/	by means of	22–24	/	1
25–27	//	numerals,	25–27	//	2
28–30	/	the number	28–30	/	1
31–33	/	or frequency	31–33	/	1
		of scores in			
		each interval.			

Go over the above procedures carefully and then go on to frame 33.

33 Before going on, let's review what you have learned about setting up a frequency table.

The first step is to find the (1) _____ of scores. This is done by (2) _____ the (3) _____ score from the (4) _____ score.

The next step is to decide on the (5) _____ of intervals you will use. After making this decision you find the size of the intervals by (6) _____ the (7) _____ by the (8) _____ of intervals.

Having set up the intervals the next thing you do is (9) _____ the number of scores in each interval and indicate the (10) _____ of scores in each interval by means of (11) _____.

(1) range	(5) number	(9) tally or count
(2) subtracting	(6) dividing	(10) number
(3) lowest	(7) range	(frequency)
(4) highest	(8) number (frequency)	(11) numerals

Review this frame carefully after you check your answers.

Now go on to frame 34.

34 Here is a partially set up frequency table. Complete it by putting in the frequencies.

5– 7	///
8–10	/////
11–13	////
14–16	//
17–19	/

5– 7	///	3
8–10	/////	5
11–13	////	4
14–16	//	2
17–19	/	1

Go on to frame 35.

35 Set up a frequency table for the following scores using 11 intervals and starting with the interval 2–3.

22, 20, 18, 18, 17, 16, 15, 14, 14, 13, 11, 10, 9, 9, 8, 7, 6, 6, 6, 5, 5, 4, 2.

2– 3	/	1		22–23	/	1
4– 5	///	3		20–21	/	1
6– 7	////	4		18–19	//	2
8– 9	///	3	Or you could also	16–17	//	2
10–11	//	2	have written:	14–15	///	3
12–13	/	1		12–13	/	1
14–15	///	3		10–11	//	2
16–17	//	2		8– 9	///	3
18–19	//	2		6– 7	////	4
20–21	/	1		4– 5	///	3
22–23	/	1		2– 3	/	1

If your answer is the same as this, go on to frame 40. If your intervals are the same as these, but your frequencies are different, then you've simply been careless about counting. Check for your error and then go on to frame 40. If your intervals are not the same as these, then go on to frame 36.

36 Let's review once more how you go about setting up a frequency table.

The first thing to do is to find the range (highest–lowest score).

Look at these scores:

28, 25, 25, 24, 20, 19, 18, 17, 16, 16, 15, 15, 13, 12, 9, 9, 7, 5, 5, 4, 2.

The range is $28-2=26$. (Remember, the range is found by subtracting the lowest score from the highest score.)

Go on to frame 36a.

36a The next step, once the range is determined, is to determine the size of your intervals. This is done by dividing the range by the number of intervals you want. (Usually, we use anywhere from 10 to 15 intervals.)

Let's say you chose to use 10 intervals. In this case, then, the size of the intervals will be (1) _____ ÷ (2) _____ = (3) _____ . (The numbers in parentheses refer to the number of the answer.)

(Remember, if your answer includes a decimal of .5 or over, you round <u>up</u>. If the decimal is less than .5, you round <u>down</u>.)

---

(1) 26   (2) 10   (3) 2.6 or 3

Go on to frame 37.

37 Now that you have determined the number and size of your intervals, the next step is to set up an interval table.

The scores once again were:

28, 25, 25, 24, 20, 19, 18, 17, 16, 16, 15, 15, 13, 12, 9, 9, 7, 5, 5, 4, 2.

The interval size is $\frac{26}{10}$ = 2.6 or <u>3</u>.

Since the lowest score is 2, the interval table must go low enough to include 2. And since the highest score is 28, the table must go high enough to include 28. Now set up the interval table.

2– 4	You'll notice that even though the table starts
5– 7	with 2 and ends with 28, it <u>does include</u> both
8–10	these values. Also note that while we chose to
11–13	start with 2, we could have started equally
14–16	well with 1. In this case, our first interval
17–19	would have been 1–3. In other words, you can
20–22	start with any score you like as long as the
23–25	lowest interval includes the lowest score.
26–28	

Go on to frame 38.

38 Now we have our intervals. The next step is to tally (count) the number of <u>scores</u> in each interval. After you have done your tallying you indicate, with numerals, the number of scores in each interval. Here are the scores once again: 28, 25, 25, 24, 20, 19, 18, 17, 16, 16, 15, 15, 13, 12, 9, 9, 7, 5, 5, 4, 2.

Now set up the interval table using 10 intervals, tally the scores, and indicate the frequency (number) of scores in each interval. Your table should be set up as illustrated below:

<u>Interval</u> <u>Tally</u> <u>Frequency</u>

Interval	Tally	Frequency
2– 4	//	2
5– 7	///	3
8–10	//	2
11–13	//	2
14–16	////	4
17–19	///	3
20–22	/	1
23–25	///	3
26–28	/	1

Go on to frame 39.

39 Here is a summary of what you have already covered concerning frequency tables.

The first step is to find the (1) _____ of scores.
This is done by (2) _____ the
(3) _____ score from the
(4) _____ score.

The next step is to decide on the (5) _____ of the intervals you will use. After making this decision you find the size of the intervals by (6) _____ the
(7) _____ by the (8) _____ of intervals.

After setting up the intervals the next thing you do is
(9) _____ the number of scores in each interval and indicate the (10) _____ of scores in each interval by means of (11) _____ .

---

(1) range   (5) number   (9) tally or count
(2) subtracting (6) dividing   (10) number or frequency
(3) lowest   (7) range   (11) numerals
(4) highest   (8) number

Go on to frame 40.

40 Find the range of the following set of scores. Also, indicate what the interval size would be if the number of intervals chosen were:

20

(a) 9; (b) 10; (c) 11; (d) 12; (e) 13; (f) 14; (g) 15.

5, 16, 1, 1, 0, 27, 3, 0, 17, 12, 4, 9, 7, 1, 1, 15, 12, 3, 5, 6, 2, 19, 4, 2, 7, 5, 18, 3, 3, 1, 7, 11.

Range = 27. (27 − 0 = 27)

Number of Intervals	Size of Interval
9	3
10	2.7 or 3 (over .5 so round up)
11	2.46 or 2 (under .5 so round down)
12	2.2 or 2
13	2.07 or 2
14	1.9 or 2
15	1.7 or 2

Go on to frame 41.

41 Using 10 intervals set up a frequency table indicating the intervals, tally and frequencies for the following set of scores:

5, 16, 1, 1, 0, 27, 3, 0, 17, 12, 4, 9, 7, 1, 1, 15, 12, 3, 5, 6, 2, 19, 4, 2, 7, 5, 18, 3, 3, 1, 7, 11.

Since you are using 10 intervals the interval size will be $\frac{27}{10} = 2.7$ or 3. Since 0 is your lowest score your first interval must start with 0.

Interval	Tally	Frequency
0– 2	/////////	9
3– 5	/////////	9
6– 8	////	4
9–11	//	2
12–14	//	2
15–17	///	3
18–20	//	2
21–23	0	0
24–26	0	0
27–29	/	1

$\underline{N}$ = 32 (where $\underline{N}$ stands for the number of scores)

Go on to frame 42.

42 Let's see how well you have mastered the concepts we've covered thus far.

Put the following scores into rank order and indicate the ranks. (You may start with the highest score as rank 1 or the lowest as rank 1.)

21, 35, 17, 43, 38, 29, 29, 36, 27, 29, 30, 35.

1	2	3	4.5	4.5	6	8	8	8	10	11	12
43,	38,	36,	35,	35,	30,	29,	29,	29,	27,	21,	17 or

1	2	3	5	5	5	7	8.5	8.5	10	11	12
17,	21,	27,	29,	29,	29,	30,	35,	35,	36,	38,	43.

You will recall that if there are tie scores the rank of these scores is an average of ranks.

If your answer is the same as this, go on to frame 43. If your answer is not the same as this, go on to frame 42a.

42a Let's go back over this concept of rank order.

As you will recall, one of the most efficient ways of handling a set of scores is to place them in (1) _____

_____ .

If, when we are assigning ranks to the scores, there are a number of scores the same, we assign to these tie scores consecutive ranks and (2) _____ these ranks and then assign this new averaged rank to all the tie scores.

---

(1) rank order
(2) average

If you answered this frame correctly, go on to frame 42b. If you did not answer this frame correctly, go back to frame 1 and review all the frames up to this point.

42b Put the following scores into rank order and indicate their ranks.

30, 34, 24, 28, 27, 26, 28, 30, 33, 29, 24, 24.

1	2	3.5	3.5	5	6.5	6.5	8	9	11	11	11
34,	33,	30,	30,	29,	28,	28,	27,	26,	24,	24,	24, or

2	2	2	4	5	6.5	6.5	8	9.5	9.5	11	12
24,	24,	24,	26,	27,	28,	28,	29,	30,	30,	33,	34

Remember, when assigning ranks to tie scores we assign consecutive ranks and then average these to find the rank for each of the tie scores.

Go on to frame 43.

43 Using the following set of scores, find the range of scores and, using 13 intervals, set up your intervals properly for a frequency table. Start your table with the score 39.

73, 61, 85, 70, 79, 58, 72, 64, 67, 81, 59, 48, 66, 92, 74, 71, 64, 82, 76, 55, 62, 39, 54, 70, 71, 62, 56, 91, 67, 84, 78, 51, 68, 83, 74, 46, 72, 58, 79, 75, 99.

The range is 99−39 = 60. Use 13 intervals and the interval size will be $\frac{60}{13}$ = 4.6 or 5.

39– 43
44– 48
49– 53
54– 58
59– 63
64– 68　　*If your answers are the same as these, go on to*
69– 73　　*frame 44. If your answers are <u>not</u> the same as*
74– 78　　*these, go on to frame 43a.*
79– 83
84– 88
89– 93
94– 98
99–103

43a You will recall that when setting up a frequency table the first step is to find the (1) _____ of scores.
This is done by (2) _____ the
(3) _____ score from the
(4) _____ score.

---

(1) range (2) subtracting (3) lowest (4) highest

If your answers are correct, go on to frame 43b. If your answers are <u>not</u> correct, go back to frame 21 and review the material from that point to this.

43b Find the range of the following set of scores:

25, 23, 27, 26, 30, 22, 21, 19, 21, 28.

The range is $30-19 = 11$.

Remember, to find the range subtract the lowest score from the highest score.

Go on to frame 43c.

43c Using the following set of scores, find the range of scores, and using 12 intervals, set up your intervals properly for a frequency table. Start your table with the score 30.

48, 56, 59, 54, 58, 58, 46, 55, 51, 64, 62, 61, 59, 38, 32, 30.

The range is $64-30 = \underline{34}$.

If you use 12 intervals, the interval size will be $\dfrac{34}{12} = 2.8$ or 3.

30−32
33−35
36−38
39−41
42−44
45−47
48−50
51−53
54−56
57−59
60−62
63−65

Go on to frame 44.

44 Here are the scores from frame 43 again. Now complete the frequency table using 13 intervals. Start your table with the interval 39—43.

73, 61, 85, 70, 79, 58, 72, 64, 67, 81, 59, 48, 66, 92, 74, 71, 64, 82, 76, 55, 62, 39, 54, 70, 71, 62, 56, 91, 67, 84, 78, 51, 68, 83, 74, 46, 72, 58, 79, 75, 99.

Intervals	Tally	Frequency
39— 43	/	1
44— 48	//	2
49— 53	/	1
54— 58	/////	5
59— 63	////	4
64— 68	//////	6
69— 73	///////	7
74— 78	/////	5
79— 83	/////	5
84— 88	//	2
89— 93	//	2
94— 98		0
99—103	/	1
		N = 41

If your answer is the same as this, then go on to frame 45. If your answer is not the same as this, then go on to frame 44a.

44a Let's review once more how you go about setting up a frequency table.

The first thing to do is to find the range.

Look at these scores:

28, 25, 25, 24, 20, 19, 18, 17, 16, 16, 15, 15, 13, 12, 9, 9, 7, 5, 5, 4, 2.

The range is 28 − 2 = 26. (Remember, the range is found by subtracting the lowest score from the highest score.)

The next step, once the range is determined, is to determine the size of your intervals. This is done by dividing the range by the number of intervals you want. (Usually, we use anywhere from 10 to 15 intervals.)

Let's say you chose to use 10 intervals. In this case, then, the size of the intervals will be (1) _____ ÷ (2) _____ = (3) _____ .

(Remember, if your answer includes a decimal of .5 or over, you round up; if less than .5, you round down.)

---

(1) 26
(2) 10
(3) 2.6 or 3

Go on to frame 44b.

44b Now that you have determined the number and size of your intervals the next step is to set up an interval table:

The scores once again were:

28, 25, 25, 24, 20, 19, 18, 17, 16, 16, 15, 15, 13, 12, 9, 9, 7, 5, 5, 4, 2.

The range is $\frac{28}{10}$ = 2.8 or 3.

Since the lowest score is 2, the interval table must go low enough to include 2. And since the highest score is 28, the table must go high enough to include 28. Now set up the interval table.

```
 2– 4
 5– 7
 8–10
11–13
14–16
17–19
20–22
23–25
26–28
```

11–13   You'll notice that even though the table starts
14–16   with 2 and ends with 28, it <u>includes</u> both these
17–19   values.

Go on to frame 44c.

44c Now we have our intervals. The next step is to tally (count) the number of <u>scores</u> in each interval. After you have done your tallying you indicate the number of scores in each interval with numerals. Here are the scores once again: 28, 25, 25, 24, 20, 19, 18, 17, 16, 16, 15, 15, 13, 12, 9, 9, 7, 5, 5, 4, 2.

Now set up the interval table using 10 intervals, tally the scores and indicate the frequency (number) of scores in each interval. Your table should be set up as illustrated below:

<u>Interval</u>   <u>Tally</u>   <u>Frequency</u>

DESCRIPTIVE STATISTICS

Interval	Tally	Frequency
2– 4	//	2
5– 7	///	3
8–10	//	2
11–13	//	2
14–16	////	4
17–19	///	3
20–22	/	1
23–25	///	3
26–28	/	1

Go on to frame 44d.

44d Before going on, let's review what you have learned, so far, about setting up a frequency table.

The first step is to find the (1) _____ of scores. This is done by (2) _____ the (3) _____ score from the (4) _____ score.

The next step is to decide on the (5) _____ of intervals you will use. After making this decision you find the size of the intervals by (6) _____ the (7) _____ by the (8) _____ of intervals.

Having set up the intervals, the next thing you do is (9) _____ the number of scores in each interval and indicate the (10) _____ of scores in each interval by means of (11) _____.

---

(1) range   (5) number   (9) tally
(2) subtracting   (6) dividing   (10) number or frequency
(3) lowest   (7) range   (11) numerals
(4) highest   (8) number

Go on to frame 44e.

44e Here are the scores from frame 43 again. Now complete the frequency table.

73, 61, 85, 70, 79, 58, 72, 64, 67, 81, 59, 48, 66, 92,
74, 71, 64, 82, 76, 55, 62, 39, 54, 70, 71, 62, 56, 91,
67, 84, 78, 51, 68, 83, 74, 46, 72, 58, 79, 75. 99.

Intervals	Tally	Frequency
39– 43	/	1
44– 48	//	2
49– 53	/	1
54– 58	/////	5
59– 63	////	4
64– 68	//////	6
69– 73	///////	7
74– 78	/////	5
79– 83	/////	5
84– 88	//	2
89– 93	//	2
94– 98		0
99–103	/	1
	$\underline{N}$ =	$\overline{41}$

Go on to frame 45.

Frequency Histograms and Frequency Polygons

45 Very often it is not enough to just set up a frequency table. We sometimes want to illustrate our distribution in order to make it more understandable.

In order to illustrate distributions we use graphs. Two kinds of graphs are most frequently used in statistics: frequency histograms and frequency polygons.

Let's take a look at a frequency histogram first.

Go on to frame 46.

FREQUENCY HISTOGRAMS

46 If we wanted to construct a histogram of the frequency distribution we set up in frame 44, we would do it in this way:

We would represent the <u>frequencies</u> along the vertical axis and the <u>scores</u> (intervals) along the horizontal axis.

Intervals	Frequency
39– 43	1
44– 48	2
49– 53	1
54– 58	5
59– 63	4
64– 68	6
69– 73	7
74– 78	5
79– 83	5
84– 88	2
89– 93	2
94– 98	0
99–103	1

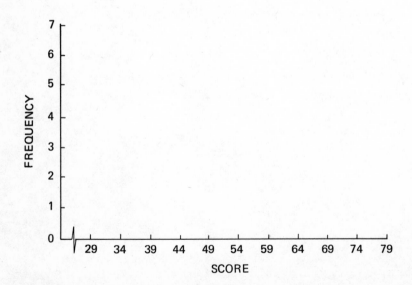

32

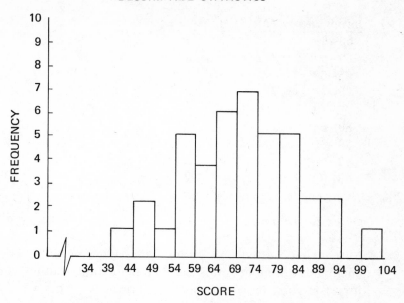

As you can see, a <u>histogram</u> is really a bar graph. The height of each rectangle indicates the frequency within the represented interval. For example, in interval 79–84, there is a frequency of 5 scores, so the bar goes across from 79–84 and up to a frequency of 5.

Go on to frame 47.

47 Using the following set of scores set up a frequency table using 9 intervals. Start with an interval whose lower limit is 55.

95, 87, 86, 85, 85, 94, 55, 62, 65, 70, 55, 59, 59, 61, 60, 73, 74, 83, 81, 92, 89, 84, 86, 63, 64, 98.

Intervals	Tally	Frequency
55–59	////	4
60–64	/////	5
65–69	/	1
70–74	///	3
75–79	0	0
80–84	///	3
85–89	//////	6
90–94	//	2
95–99	//	2
		$\underline{N = 26}$

Go on to frame 48.

48 Now, using the frequency table you have just prepared, construct a histogram of the frequency distribution. Before you start look at frame 46 again.

Remember, a histogram is a bar graph with the frequencies along the <u>vertical axis</u> and the scores (intervals) along the <u>horizontal axis</u>.

Note: Since there were no scores in the interval 75–79, there is no bar over this interval.

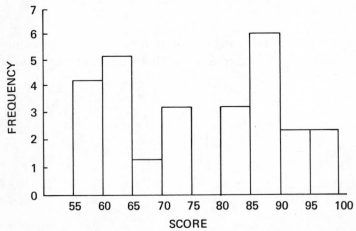

Go on to frame 49.

34

FREQUENCY POLYGONS

49 Often, we find it more convenient to use, instead of a histogram, a <u>polygon</u>. A <u>frequency polygon</u> is really a line
graph. In this case, instead of putting bars over the interval to indicate the frequency, we merely put a dot over
the midpoint of the interval at the required height and
then join all the dots to get our line graph.

As an example, let's convert the histogram from frame 48
to a polygon.

As you can see, joining the midpoints of the intervals has
resulted in a line graph. Note that since there are no
scores in the interval 75–79, the line hits the horizontal
axis at this point.

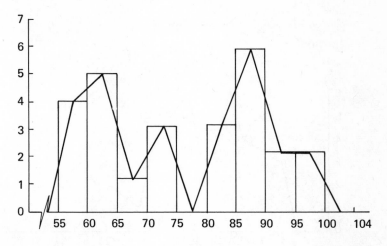

Go on to frame 50.

50 Using the following set of scores, set up a frequency table, starting with the score 4 and using 9 intervals. Then construct a frequency polygon. (Start with an interval whose lower limit is 4.) Before you start look at frame 49 again.

30, 25, 25, 23, 21, 20, 20, 19, 18, 18, 17, 16, 16, 16, 15, 14, 12, 11, 11, 10, 10, 10, 9, 8, 7, 7, 6, 5, 5.

Interval	Tally	Frequency
4– 6	///	3
7– 9	////	4
10–12	collection//////	6
13–15	//	2
16–18	collection//////	6
19–21	////	4
22–24	/	1
25–27	//	2
28–30	/	1
		N = 29

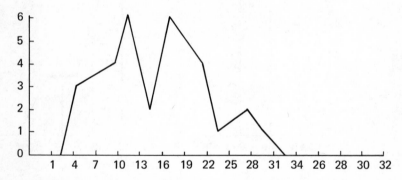

Go on to frame 51.

51 Using the following scores, set up a frequency table (starting with score of 1 and using 11 intervals) and construct <u>both</u> a frequency histogram <u>and</u> a frequency polygon. Before you start look at frame 49 again.

22, 20, 18, 18, 17, 16, 15, 14, 14, 13, 11, 10, 9, 9, 8, 7, 6, 6, 6, 5, 5, 4, 2.

Interval	Tally	Frequency
1– 2	/	1
3– 4	/	1
5– 6	/////	5
7– 8	//	2
9–10	///	3
11–12	/	1
13–14	///	3
15–16	//	2
17–18	///	3
19–20	/	1
21–22	/	1

$$\underline{N} = 23$$

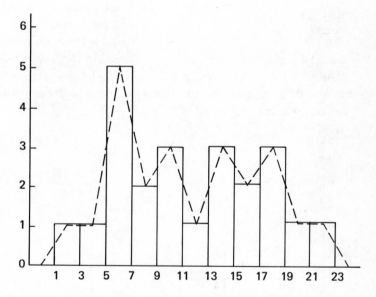

If your answers are the same as these, go on to frame 58. If your answers are not the same as these, go on to frame 52.

52 To construct a <u>histogram</u> we first set up a frequency table.

Intervals	Tally	Frequency
40– 44	/	1
45– 49	//	2
50– 54	/	1
55– 59	/////	5
60– 64	////	4
65– 69	//////	6
70– 74	///////	7
75– 79	/////	5
80– 84	/////	5
85– 89	//	2
90– 94	//	2
95– 99		0
100–103	/	1

N = 41

After we set up the frequency table, the next step is to set up the graph. In doing this we represent the frequencies along the vertical axis and the scores (intervals) along the horizontal axis.

As you can see, a <u>histogram</u> is really a bar graph. The height of each rectangle indicates the frequency within the represented interval. For example, in interval 79–84 there is a frequency of 4 scores, so the bar goes across from 79–84 and up to a frequency of 4.

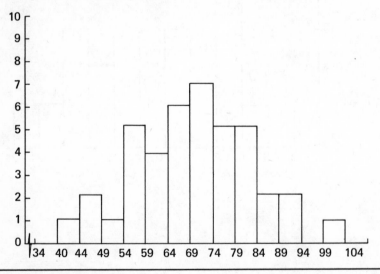

Go on to frame 53.

53 Using the following set of scores set up a frequency table using 9 intervals. Start with an interval whose lower limit is 55.

95, 87, 86, 85, 85, 94, 55, 62, 65, 70, 55, 59, 59, 61, 60, 73, 74, 83, 81, 92, 89, 84, 86, 63, 64.

Intervals	Tally	Frequency
55−59	////	4
60−64	/////	5
65−69	/	1
70−74	///	3
75−79	0	0
80−84	///	3
85−89	固//////	6
90−94	//	2
95−99	/	1
		N = 25

Go on to frame 54.

54 Now, using the frequency table you have just prepared, construct a histogram of the frequency distribution.

Remember, a histogram is a bar graph with the frequencies along the <u>vertical axis</u> and the scores (intervals) along the <u>horizontal axis</u>. Before you start, look at frame 46 again.

Note: Since there were no
scores in the interval
75–79, there is no bar
over this interval.

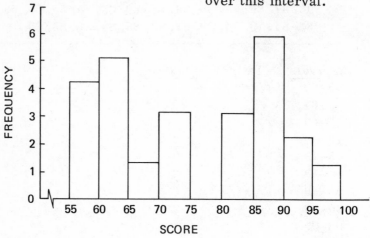

SCORE

Go on to frame 55.

55 Frequently we find it more convenient to use a <u>polygon</u>
instead of a histogram. A <u>frequency polygon</u> is really a
line graph. In this case, instead of putting bars over the
interval to indicate the frequency, we merely put a dot
over the midpoint of the interval at the required height and
then join all the dots to get our line graph.

As an example, let's convert the histogram from frame 48
to a polygon.

As you can see, joining the <u>midpoints</u> of the intervals has
resulted in a line graph. Note that since there are no
scores in the interval 75–79, the line hits the horizontal
axis at this point.

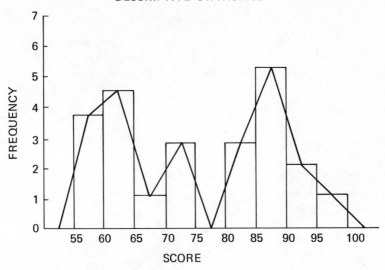

Go on to frame 56.

56 Set up a frequency table for the following set of scores, then construct a frequency polygon. In setting up your table, use 9 intervals starting with the score 4.

30, 25, 25, 23, 21, 20, 20, 19, 18, 18, 17, 16, 16, 16, 15, 14, 12, 11, 11, 10, 10, 10, 9, 8, 7, 7, 6, 5, 5.

Before you start you might look at frame 49 again.

Interval	Tally	Frequency
4– 6	///	3
7– 9	////	4
10–12	//////	6
13–15	//	2
16–18	//////	6
19–21	////	4
22–24	/	1
25–27	//	2
28–30	/	1

$$\underline{N} = \overline{29}$$

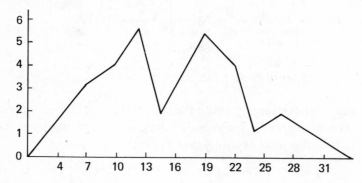

Go on to frame 57.

Go on to frame 57.

57 Using the following scores, set up a frequency table and construct <u>both</u> a frequency histogram <u>and</u> a frequency polygon. Start your table with an interval whose lower limit is 2 and use 11 intervals.

> 22, 20, 18, 18, 17, 16, 15, 14, 14, 13, 11, 10, 9,
> 9, 8, 7, 6, 6, 6, 5, 5, 4, 2.

Before you start on the histogram and polygon you may, if you wish, look at frame 55 again.

DESCRIPTIVE STATISTICS

Interval	Tally	Frequency
2– 3	/	1
4– 5	///	3
6– 7	////	4
8– 9	///	3
10–11	//	2
12–13	/	1
14–15	///	3
16–17	//	2
18–19	//	2
20–21	/	1
22–23	/	1

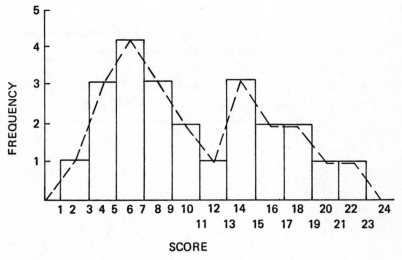

Go on to frame 58.

58 From the following set of scores set up a frequency table. Use an interval size of 3 and start with a lower limit of 37.

59, 56, 53, 50, 51, 47, 47, 43, 44, 44, 42, 41, 40, 37, 37, 38, 39, 39, 38, 38.

Intervals	Tally	Frequency
58–60	/	1
55–57	/	1
52–54	/	1
49–51	//	2
46–48	//	2
43–45	///	3
40–42	///	3
37–39	///////	7

You will notice that in this item the intervals are arranged with the highest scores at the top and the lowest at the bottom. This is the reverse of the procedure to this point. A frequency table may be set up either way.

If your answer is the same as the one above, go on to frame 59.

If your answer is not the same as the one above, go back to frame 25 and work up to this point again.

59 Using the frequency table from frame 58, construct both a frequency histogram and a frequency polygon.

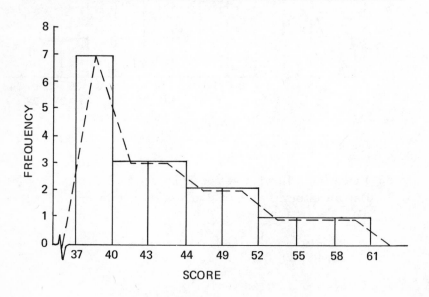

If your answer is the same as the one above, go on to frame 60.

If your answer is <u>not</u> the same as the one above, go back to frame 46 and go over the material to this point again.

Median, Mean, and Mode

60 A question we frequently ask is: "Is this behavior representative of this person or group?" To answer such a question we look not at just one sample of behavior but at several samples of behavior, in order to achieve an estimate of the individual's or group's most expected behavior.

To obtain such an estimate, depending on our purpose, we can make use of either of two measures of central or focal tendency.

These two measures are the <u>median</u> and the <u>mean</u>.

Another measure used to compare groups is the <u>mode</u>. While this is not a measure of central tendency in the same sense that the mean and median are, it is commonly considered along with these measures.

Go on to frame 60a.

60a When we talk of a measure of central tendency, then, we are referring generally to that score about which all the other scores tend to cluster (some being above it and some below). In other words, we are referring to that score which provides us with a "quantitative index" of the location of our distribution of scores.

For example, if we wanted to know what an individual's most typical running speed was, we would time him over several runs, rather than just one, and then look for the score which seems most representative of the whole series.

Of course, some of his scores will be above this "focal" score and some will be below it.

Go on to frame 61.

61 The two measures of central tendency are the <u>median</u> and the <u>mean</u>.

The <u>median</u> refers to that score or point above and below which 50% of the scores fall. In other words, if you had 100 scores, 50 would lie above the median and 50 below.

The <u>mean</u> refers to the arithmetic average of all the scores. The mean might be defined as the point in the distribution corresponding to the sum of the scores divided by the number of scores.

Both the median and the mean are measures of the size of scores.

The <u>mode</u>, on the other hand, refers to the most common or frequently obtained score; that is, the score obtained by more individuals than any other score in the distribution.

Go on to frame 62.

62 When we look for an individual's or group's most representative score, we look for that score about which all the others tend to _____.

---

cluster or gather

Go on to frame 62a.

62a The score or point about which the other scores tend to cluster is referred to as a _____ of _____ _____.

---

measure of central tendency

Go on to frame 62b.

62b Two measures of central tendency are:

  (1) _____
  (2) _____

The most frequently obtained score is called the

  (3) _____ .

_____

  (1) mean or median
  (2) mean or median
  (3) mode

Go on to frame 62c.

62c The mode refers to that score which is the most

  _____ _____ .

_____

  frequently obtained

Go on to frame 62d.

62d The median refers to that score above and below which
  _____ of the scores fall.

_____

  50% (or half)

Go on to frame 62e.

62e The mean refers to the _____
  _____ of the scores.

_____

  arithmetic average

Go on to frame 63.

63 The mode, remember, refers to the most popular or most
  frequently obtained score.

Find the modal score in the following set of scores.

28, 27, 29, 30, 24, 23, 28, 31, 25, 28, 20.

The modal score is 28 since more individuals obtained a score of 28 than any other score.

Go on to frame 64.

64 The <u>median</u> score or point (since there may well be no median score but rather just a point in the distribution) is that score or point above and below which 50% of the distribution of scores lie.

For example, take the following scores:

25, 24, 23, 22, 21, 20, 19, 18.

The median value is 21.5 since this is halfway between the two middle scores 22 and 21.

Go on to frame 65.

FINDING THE MEDIAN

65 One way to find the median is to rank order the scores and simply find the midpoint of the rank ordered set of scores.

For example:

11, 10, 9, 7, 6, 5, 3, 2, 1.

These scores are rank ordered. There are 9 scores so the halfway point would be the fifth score or the score, 6.

Rank order the following scores and find the median:

24, 23, 25, 27, 30, 21, 18, 17, 22, 26, 14, 15, 16.

14 15 16 17 18 21 22 23 24 25 26 27 30

21.5

When we rank order the scores we get: 30, 27, 26, 25, 24, 23, 22, 21, 18, 17, 16, 15, 14.

Counting halfway up the set of scores, we find the score 22 to be the midscore or median.

Go on to frame 66.

66 Find the median of the following set of scores:

   45, 46, 50, 40, 42, 39, 51, 49, 47, 48, 37, 35, 52, 53, 38.

When the scores are rank ordered we get:

   53, 52, 51, 50, 49, 48, 47, 46, 45, 42, 40, 39, 38, 37, 35.

The halfway point in this distribution is the eighth score or the score 46. The median, therefore, is 46.

Go on to frame 67.

67   54, 48, 50, 52, 51, 44, 47, 46, 39, 43, 41, 42, 35, 38, 37

The median of the above set of scores is (1) _____ . It is the median because it is the (2) _____ score.

---

(1) 44
(2) middle or midpoint

Go on to frame 68.

68 So far we have looked only at distributions with odd numbers of scores (13 scores, 15 scores, etc.). If the distribution has an even number of scores (for example, 16 scores), the median is still halfway through the distribution, but now it is a point rather than a score.

In this case, the median is found by finding the point midway between the middle 2 scores of the distribution.

Go on to frame 69.

69 Look at this set of scores:

$$15, 14, 13, 12, 10, 9, 7, 6, 5, 4.$$

Since there is an even number of scores, the median must lie midway between the middle 2 scores. In this distribution the middle 2 scores are 10 and 9. The point halfway between them is $\dfrac{10 + 9}{2}$ or 9.5. 9.5 is, therefore, the median of the above distribution.

Find the median for this distribution. (Remember, you have to rank order the scores first.)

$$20, 21, 18, 17, 23, 16, 15, 24, 27, 26$$

Since there is an even number of scores, the median will lie halfway between the middle 2 scores which are 21 and 20. The median, therefore, is $\dfrac{21 + 20}{2}$ or 20.5.

If your answer is 20.5, go on to frame 71.
If your answer is not 20.5, go on to frame 70.

70 As you will recall, when the distribution has either an odd number of scores or an even number of scores, the median is halfway. However, when the distribution has an even number of scores, the median may be a point rather than a score.

In this case, the median is found by finding the point midway between the middle 2 scores of the distribution.

Go on to frame 70a.

70a Look at this set of scores:

$$18, 16, 15, 14, 13, 12, 11, 9, 7, 6, 5, 4.$$

Here we have an even number of scores. The median, therefore, must lie midway between the middle 2 scores. In this distribution the middle 2 scores are 11 and 12. The point halfway between them is $\dfrac{11 + 12}{2}$ or 11.5.

Therefore, 11.5 is the median of the above distribution. Find the median for this distribution. (Remember, you have to rank order the scores first.)

$$22, 23, 18, 17, 25, 16, 15, 24, 27, 26$$

Because there is an even number of scores, the median will lie halfway between the middle 2 scores which are 22 and 23. The median, therefore, is $\dfrac{22 + 23}{2}$ or 22.5.

Go on to frame 71.

71 Find the median of the following set of scores:

$$97, 87, 94, 90, 86, 86, 88, 93, 82, 85, 95, 92, 81, 80.$$

Since there is an even number of scores (14), the median lies midway between the 2 middle scores which are 88 and 87. Therefore, the median is $\dfrac{88 + 87}{2} = 87.5$.

Note: Even though there are 2 scores of 87, these occupy the sixth and seventh positions. The median lies between the seventh and eighth scores; i.e., 87 and 88.

Go on to frame 72.

72 Since the median is the midpoint in the distribution of scores, what do you think will happen if you were to add an odd number of scores to the distribution?

For example, take the scores: 8, 7, 6, 5, 4, 3, 2. The median is 5. Now if we add the scores 9, 10, and 1, what happens to the median? That is, would the median change and, if so, in what direction?

The median changes. In this case, it moves up because we added 2 scores to the top and only 1 score to the bottom of the distribution.

Go on to frame 73.

73 What would happen to the median if we were to add the same number of scores to the top and bottom of the distribution?

For example, consider the same scores as in frame 72:

8, 7, 6, 5, 4, 3, 2.

If we were to add the scores 9, 10, 1 and 0, what would happen to the median? That is, would the median change and, if so, in what direction?

It would remain the same; that is, the median would still be 5 since 5 is still the midscore of the distribution.

Go on to frame 74.

74 Before going on, let's review some of the concepts we've covered to this point.

The two measures of central tendency are the
(1) _____ and (2) _____ .

The most common or frequently obtained score is the
(3) _____ .

---

(1) (2) mean, median (either order) (3) mode.

If your answer is the same as this, go on to frame 77.
If your answer is not the same as this, go on to frame 75.

75 The <u>mode</u> refers to the most common or frequently obtained score; that is, it is the score obtained by more individuals than any other score in the distribution.

The <u>median</u> refers to that score or point above and below which 50% of the scores fall. In other words, if you had 100 scores, 50 would lie above the median and 50 below.

The <u>mean</u> refers to the <u>arithmetic average</u> of all the scores.

Go on to frame 76.

76 Given the following set of scores:

$$15, 14, 13, 12, 10, 9, 8.$$

The median is (1) _____ .

If the scores 19, 18, 17 and 7 were added, the median would be (2) _____ .

If the scores 19, 18, 17, 7, 6 and 5 were added, the median would be (3) _____ .

(1) 12
(2) 13
(3) 12

If your answers are correct, go on to frame 77.
If your answers are <u>not</u> correct, go on to frame 76a.

76a If we add the same number of scores at the top and bottom of the distribution, the median will remain the same because it will still be the <u>middle</u> point.

However, if the distribution has more scores added to either the top or bottom, the median will move either up or down, as the case may be, because the median must be the <u>middle</u> point of the distribution.

Go on to frame 77.

77 The mode is the (1) _____ _____ score.

The median is the point above and below which
(2) _____ of the scores lie.

The mean is the (3) _____
_____ of the distribution of scores.

---

(1) most common (or most frequent)
(2) 50% or half
(3) arithmetic average

Go on to frame 78.

78   23, 22, 21, 20, 19, 19, 18, 17, 15, 15, 15, 16, 14, 12, 10

What is the modal score of the above distribution?
(1) _____

What is the median of the above distribution? (2) _____

---

(1) 15
(2) 17

If both your answers are correct, go on to frame 85.
If only answer (1) is correct, go on to frame 80.
If only answer (2) is correct, go on to frame 79.
If both answers are incorrect, work through all the
frames from 79 to 85.

79 The <u>mode</u>, remember, refers to the most popular or most
frequently obtained score.

Find the modal score in the following set of scores.

      28, 27, 29, 30, 24, 23, 28, 31, 25, 28, 20

The modal score is 28 since more individuals obtained a
score of 28 than any other score.

Go on to frame 80.

80 The <u>median</u> score or point is that score or point above
and below which 50% of the distribution of scores lie.

For example, in the following scores, the median value is
41.5 since this is halfway between the 2 middle scores 42
and 41:

45, 44, 43, 42, 41, 40, 39, 38.

Go on to frame 81.

81 To find the median, rank order the scores and simply find
the midpoint of that rank-ordered set of scores.

For example:

11, 10, 9, 7, 6, 5, 3, 2, 1.

These scores are rank ordered. There are 11 scores so
the halfway point would be the fifth score or the score 6.

Rank order the following scores and find the median.

14, 13, 15, 17, 20, 11, 8, 7, 12, 16, 4, 5, 6

When we rank order the scores we get:

20, 17, 16, 15, 14, 13, 12, 11, 8, 7, 6, 5, 4.

Counting halfway up the set of scores we find the score <u>12</u>
to be the midscore or median.

Go on to frame 82.

82 54, 48, 50, 52, 51, 44, 47, 46, 39, 43, 41, 42, 35, 38, 37

The <u>median</u> of the above set of scores is (1) _____ . It is
the median because it is the (2) _____
score.

---

(1) 44
(2) middle or midpoint

Go on to frame 83.

83 Remember, the median is always the score or point midway through a distribution of scores.

Go on to frame 84.

84 If we add the same number of scores at the top and bottom of the distribution, the median will remain the same because it will still be the middle point.

However, if the distribution has more scores added to either the top or bottom the median will move either up or down, as the case may be, because the median must be the middle point of the distribution.

Go on to frame 85.

FINDING THE MEAN

85 The second, and in many ways the most widely used, measure of central tendency is the mean.

The mean (by convention the symbol $\bar{X}$ is used to stand for the mean) is the arithmetic average of a set of scores.

Go on to frame 86.

86 Since $\overline{X}$ (symbol for mean) is the arithmetic average of a distribution of scores, one way to find it is to simply <u>sum</u> the scores and divide by the number of scores in the distribution.

For example, in order to find $\overline{X}$ we sum the given scores $(15 + 12 + 11 + 10 + 9 + 8 + 5 = 70)$ and then divide by 7 (the number of scores). $\dfrac{70}{7} = 10$.

Thus, $\overline{X} = 10$ for the above scores.

Find $\overline{X}$ for these scores: 20, 21, 18, 17, 19, 14, 12.

Since $\overline{X}$ is the <u>sum</u> of the scores <u>divided</u> by the number of scores, $\overline{X}$ in this case is:

$$\frac{20 + 21 + 18 + 17 + 19 + 14 + 12}{7} = \frac{121}{7} = 17.3$$

Go on to frame 86a.

86a The symbol for the mean is (1) _____.

One way to find the mean is to find the (2) _____ of all the scores and then to (3) _____ by the (4) _____ of scores.

---

(1) $\overline{X}$ (3) divide

(2) sum   (4) number

Go on to frame 87.

87 There are several other symbols we use for convenience sake. Let's look at these before going any further.

We use the symbol X to stand for a single score. So, if we wanted to represent the fact that we are adding 4 scores, we would do so in this way:

$$X_1 + X_2 + X_3 + X_4,$$

where X with the subscript 1 stands for the first score; X with subscript 2 stands for the second score; and so on.

When we add the scores, we get their <u>sum</u>. To represent the fact that we have a sum of scores, we use the symbol Σ for the sum and X for all the individual scores. So, to represent the fact that when adding a set of scores we get a <u>sum</u> of scores we use:

$$X_1 + X_2 + X_3 + X_4 = \Sigma X.$$

This reads the first score plus the second plus the third plus the fourth equals the <u>sum</u> of scores.

Go on to frame 87a.

87a To represent a single score we use the symbol
(1) _____.

To represent a <u>sum of scores</u> we use the symbol
(2) _____.

---

(1) X
(2) ΣX

Go on to frame 87b.

87b We represent the fact that when we add the first score plus the second plus the third plus the fourth, we get a sum of scores by the symbols

_____ + _____ + _____ + _____ = _____.

$X_1 + X_2 + X_3 + X_4 = \Sigma X$

Go on to frame 87c.

87c To represent the number of people in the distribution we use the symbol N. For example, if we wanted to indicate that we have scores for 10 people, we would do so by:

$$N = 10$$

How would we express the fact that we have scores for 40 people?

$N = 40$

Go on to frame 87d.

87d Since the $\overline{X}$ is found by first finding the sum of scores and then dividing by the number of scores (that is, the number of people for whom we have scores), we would represent this fact by:

$$\overline{X} = \frac{\Sigma X}{N} \quad \text{(mean equals the sum of scores divided by the number of scores)}$$

Go on to frame 88.

88 We represent the number of people in our sample (that is, the number of people for whom we have scores) by means of the symbol N. So, if we have scores for 15 people, $N = 15$.

The symbol ΣX stands for (1) _____ of
(2) _____ .

The symbol N stands for the (3) _____ of
(4) _____ for whom we have scores.

---

(1) sum   (3) number
(2) scores   (4) people

Go on to frame 89.

89 To represent the mean or arithmetic average we use the symbol $\overline{X}$.

Find $\overline{X}$ for the following distribution:

$$10, 15, 12, 9, 11, 8, 6, 7, 5.$$

$\overline{X} = 9.2$

To find $\overline{X}$, the arithmetic average, we sum the scores and divide by the number of scores. Therefore, $\overline{X} = \dfrac{\Sigma X}{N}$ or $\dfrac{83}{9}$ = 9.22 which we round down to 9.2 since the second decimal is less than 5.

Go on to frame 90.

90   20, 21, 25, 19, 18, 20, 15, 25, 30, 28, 29

Find ΣX, N and $\overline{X}$ for the above distribution of scores. (If you've forgotten what these symbols stand for, look at frames 86 and 87 again.)

$\Sigma X = 250$
$N = 11$
$\overline{X} = \dfrac{\Sigma X}{N} = \dfrac{250}{11} = \underline{22.7}$

Go on to frame 91.

91 Complete the equation expressing the value of $\overline{X}$.

$$\overline{X} = \underline{\hspace{3cm}}.$$

$\overline{X} = \dfrac{\Sigma X}{N}$

Go on to frame 92.

92 30, 31, 35, 40, 39, 38, 25, 27, 28, 30

Given the above scores indicate which of the following is:
(1) ΣX; (2) $\bar{X}$; (3) N.

10; 323; 32.3

---

(1) $\Sigma X = 323$; (2) $\bar{X} = 32.3$; (3) $N = 10$.

If your answers are the same as these, go on to frame 97.
If your answers are not the same as these, go on to frame
93.

93 Four symbols are used frequently in statistics. These are:

$$X; \bar{X}; \Sigma X; \text{ and } N.$$

The symbol X is used to stand for a single score. So, if
we wanted to represent the fact that we are adding four
scores, we would do so in this way:

$$X_1 + X_2 + X_3 + X_4,$$

where X with the subscript 1 stands for the first score; X
with the subscript 2 stands for the second score; and so on.

When the scores are added, we get their sum. We use the
symbol Σ to represent a sum of scores and X for each
score. So, to represent the fact that when we add a set of
scores we get a sum of scores, we use:

$$X_1 + X_2 + X_3 + X_4 = \Sigma X.$$

This reads the first score plus the second score plus the
third score plus the fourth score equals the sum of
scores.

Go on to frame 94.

94 The number of people for whom we have scores is represented by the symbol N. So, if we have scores for 25 people, $N = 25$.

The symbol ΣX stands for the (1) _____ of (2) _____ .

The symbol N stands for the (3) _____ of (4) _____ for whom we have scores.

---

(1) sum   (3) number
(2) scores   (4) people

Go on to frame 95.

95 The mean or arithmetic average is represented by the symbol $\bar{X}$.

Find $\bar{X}$ for the following distribution:

$$20, 25, 22, 19, 21, 18, 16, 17, 15.$$

$\bar{X} = \underline{19.2}$

To find $\bar{X}$, the arithmetic average, we sum the scores and divide by the number of scores. Therefore, $\bar{X} = \dfrac{\Sigma X}{N}$ or $\dfrac{173}{9}$ = 19.22 which we round down to 19.2 since the second decimal is less than 5.

Go on to frame 96.

96   40, 38, 35, 42, 51, 36, 35

Given the above scores, indicate which of the following is:
(1) ΣX; (2) $\bar{X}$; and (3) N.

$$7; \quad 277; \quad 39.6$$

---

(1) $\Sigma X = 277$; (2) $\bar{X} = 39.6$; (3) $N = 7$.

Go on to frame 97.

97 Given the distribution:

> 50, 51, 45, 30, 31, 32, 34, 36, 40, 42, 45, 51, 47,
> 31, 33, 50, 55, 40, 39.

What is ΣX? (1) _____

What is N? (2) _____

What is $\overline{X}$? (3) _____

(If you have forgotten what these symbols stand for, look at frames 86 and 87 again.)

___

(1) $\Sigma X = 782$
(2) $N = 19$
(3) $\overline{X} = 41.2$

Go on to frame 98.

98 Before we go on, do you remember what the two measures of central tendency are?

The two measures of central tendency are the:
(1) _____ and (2) _____ .

What is the measure of the most common score?
(3) _____

___

(1) median
(2) mean (either order)
(3) mode

Go on to frame 99.

99 When we talked about the median, we looked at the effect on the median of adding scores to either (or both) the top half or bottom half of the distribution.

Now let's see what happens to the mean when we add scores to the distribution.

Given the scores 25, 24, 24, 23, 20, 19, 18, 18, 17, 15, 14, 10, 10, 8. The mean of these scores will be (1) _____ .

What will the mean be if we add the score 30? (2) _____

If we add the score 5, the mean will be (3) _____.

(If you have forgotten how to find the mean, look at frame 87 d.)

_____

(1) $\bar{X} = 17.5$
(2) $\bar{X} = 18.3$
(3) $\bar{X} = 16.7$

Go on to frame 100.

100 As you see, adding a score to the top of the distribution moves $\bar{X}$ up. Adding a score to the bottom of the distribution moves $\bar{X}$ down. Note, though, that as long as the scores we add are neither too much higher than the top score nor too much lower than the bottom score, the mean shifts only a little.

Now look at these same scores again:

25, 24, 24, 23, 20, 19, 18, 18, 17, 15, 14, 10, 10, 8.

Suppose this time we add the score 55 to the other scores. Now, $\bar{X}$ will be (1) _____?

Suppose we add the score 1. Now, $\bar{X}$ will be (2) _____?

_____

(1) $\bar{X} = 20$
(2) $\bar{X} = 16.4$

Go on to frame 101.

101 Use the same set of scores.

25, 24, 24, 23, 20, 19, 18, 18, 17, 15, 14, 10, 10, 8

Suppose this time we add to the other scores the score 85. Now, $\bar{X}$ will be _____. (Remember, the mean is found like this: $\bar{X} = \dfrac{\text{sum of scores}}{\text{number of scores}}$.)

_____

22

Go on to frame 101a.

101a As you have seen, the more <u>extreme</u> the score that is added to the distribution the greater the shift will be in the mean.

You will remember that when we added just one score, no matter how extreme, the <u>median</u> shifted only a little because it expresses just the midpoint of the distribution, <u>not</u> the average.

This then illustrates the fact that the mean is much more sensitive to extremely high and extremely low scores than is the median and will reflect this by moving either up or down <u>more</u> than will the median.

Go on to frame 102.

102 If we were to add an extremely high score to the distribution, the mean would shift (1) _____
(2) _____ than the median.

If we were to add an extremely low score to the distribution, the mean would shift (3) _____
(4) _____ than the median.

---

(1) up
(2) more
(3) down
(4) more

If your answers are the same as these, go on to frame 103.
If your answers are <u>not</u> the same as these, go on to frame 102a.

102a Let's take another look at what happens to the mean when we add scores to the distribution.

Given the scores 25, 24, 24, 23, 20, 19, 18, 18, 16, 15, 14, 10, 10, 8, The mean of these scores will be (1) _____.

What will the mean be if we add the score 28? (2) _____

If we add the score 4, the mean will be (3) _____.

---

(1) 17.4; (2) 18.2; (3) 16.6

Go on to frame 102b.

102b As you see, adding a score to either the top or bottom half of the distribution moves $\overline{X}$ up or down. However, as long as the added score is not very much higher or lower than the rest of the scores, the mean will shift only a little.

Now look at these scores again:

  25, 24, 24, 23, 20, 19, 18, 18, 17, 15, 14, 10, 10, 8.

This time suppose we add the score 60, $\overline{X}$ will be (1) _____.

Suppose we add the score 1, $\overline{X}$ will be (2) _____.

---

(1) 20.3
(2) 16.3

Go on to frame 102c.

102c Let's use the same set of scores.

  25, 24, 24, 23, 20, 19, 18, 18, 17, 15, 14, 10, 10, 8.

Suppose this time we add the score 90; $\overline{X}$ will now be _____.

22.3

Go on to frame 102d.

67

102d As you have seen, the more extreme the score that is added to the distribution, the greater the shift will be in the mean.

When we added just one score, no matter how extreme, the median shifted only a little because it expresses just the <u>midpoint</u> of the distribution <u>not</u> the average.

The mean is much more sensitive to extremely high and extremely low scores than is the median.

Go on to frame 103.

103 Find the mode, median and mean of the following set of scores:

> 22, 20, 19, 18, 17, 17, 16, 15, 14, 13, 13, 12, 11, 11, 11, 10.

The mode is (1) _____ .

The median is (2) _____ .

The mean is (3) _____ .

(1) 11
(2) 14.5
(3) 14.9

If all three of your answers are the same as these, go on to frame 115.
If only answers 2 and 3 are the same, go on to frame 113.
If only answer 3 is the same, go on to frame 109.
If only answers 1 and 2 are the same, go on to frame 104.
If all three answers are <u>not</u> the same, go on to frame 104.

104 Since $\overline{X}$ (symbol for mean) is the average of a distribution of scores, one way to find it is to simply sum the scores and divide by the number of scores in the distribution.

Example: Given the scores 15, 12, 11, 10, 9, 8, 5, find the sum, $\overline{X}$, of these scores.

$$15 + 12 + 11 + 10 + 9 + 8 + 5 = 70$$

Divide by 7 (the number of scores).

$$\frac{70}{7} = \underline{10}$$

Thus, $\overline{X} = 10$ for the above scores.

Find $\overline{X}$ for these scores: 20, 21, 18, 17, 19, 14, 12.

Since $\overline{X}$ is the sum of the scores divided by the number of scores, $\overline{X}$ in this case is:

$$\frac{20 + 21 + 18 + 17 + 19 + 14 + 12}{7} = \frac{121}{7} = 17.3$$

Go on to frame 105.

105 To represent the mean or arithmetic average we use the symbol $\overline{X}$.

Find $\overline{X}$ for the following distribution:

$$10, 15, 12, 9, 11, 8, 6, 7, 5.$$

$\overline{X} = \underline{9.2}$

To find $\overline{X}$ or the arithmetic average we sum the scores and divide by the number of scores. Therefore, $\overline{X} = \frac{\Sigma X}{N}$ or $\frac{83}{9}$ = 9.22 which we round down to 9.2 since the second decimal is less than 5.

Go on to frame 106.

106   20, 21, 25, 19, 18, 20, 15, 25, 30, 28, 29

Find ΣX, N and $\overline{X}$ for the above distribution of scores.

$\Sigma X = 250$

$N = 11$

$\overline{X} = \dfrac{\Sigma X}{N} = \dfrac{250}{11} = \underline{22.7}$

Go on to frame 107.

107 Complete the equation for the value of $\overline{X}$.

$$\overline{X} = \underline{\qquad}.$$

$\overline{X} = \dfrac{\Sigma X}{N}$

Go on to frame 108.

108 Given the distribution:

> 50, 51, 45, 30, 31, 32, 34, 36, 40, 42, 45, 51,
> 47, 31, 33, 50, 55, 40, 39.

What is ΣX? (1) _____

What is N?   (2) _____

What is $\overline{X}$?   (3) _____

---

(1) 782
(2) 19
(3) 41.2

If you did not get (1) and (2) in frame 103 correct, go on to frame 109.

If you did get (1) and (2) correct in frame 103, go on to frame 115.

109 The median is found by finding the score or point which is midway in the distribution of scores.

Go on to frame 110.

110 Find the median of the following set of scores.

97, 87, 94, 90, 86, 87, 88, 93, 82, 85, 95, 92, 81, 80

The median lies midway between the middle 2 scores which are 88 and 87. Therefore, the median is $\dfrac{88 + 87}{2}$ = 87.5.

Go on to frame 111.

111 Since the median is the midpoint in the distribution of scores, what do you think will happen if you add an odd number of scores to the distribution?

For example, given the scores 8, 7, 6, 5, 4, 3, 2, the median is 5. Now if you add the scores 9, 10 and 1, what happens to the median?

The median changes, in this case. It moves up because we added 2 scores to the top and only one to the bottom of the distribution.

Go on to frame 112.

112 What would happen to the median if we were to add the same number of scores to the top and bottom of the distribution?

For example, take the scores in frame 111: 8, 7, 6, 5, 4, 3, 2. If we were to add the scores 9, 10, 1 and 0, what would happen to the median?

It would remain the same; i.e., the median would still be 5 since 5 is <u>still</u> the midscore of the distribution.

If you did <u>not</u> get the correct mode in frame 103, go on to frame 113.

If you <u>did</u> get the correct mode in frame 103, go on to frame 115.

113 The two measures of central tendency, again, are the median and the mean.

The median refers to that score or point above and below which 50% of the scores fall. In other words, if you had 100 scores, 50 would lie above the median and 50 below.

The mean refers to the arithmetic average of all the scores.

The mode, however, refers to the most popular or frequently obtained score, that is, the score obtained by more individuals than any other score in the distribution.

Go on to frame 114.

114 The mode refers to the most popular or most frequently obtained score.

Find the modal score in the following set of scores:

28, 27, 29, 30, 24, 23, 28, 31, 25, 28, 20.

The modal score is 28 since more individuals obtained a score of 28 than any other score.

Go on to frame 115.

Deviation Scores

DEVIATION SCORES FROM RAW SCORES

115 For the following set of scores the mean is 15.1.

20, 20, 19, 18, 15, 15, 14, 12, 10, 8.

Note that none of these scores is the same as the mean. In other words, each differs (that is, "deviates") from the mean.

In distribution of scores, many scores will <u>deviate</u> from the mean.

Go on to frame 115a.

115a Scores 20, 20, 19, 18, 15, 15, 14, 12, 10, 8 are said to _____ from the mean which is 15.1.

---

deviate

Go on to frame 116.

116 Scores that <u>deviate</u> from the mean are those scores which are _____ from the mean.

---

different

Go on to frame 116a.

116a Since most scores deviate from the mean, there will be a difference between any score and the mean. This difference is called a deviation score.

A deviation score indicates the amount by which any score differs, or deviates, from the mean.

Go on to frame 116b.

116b Every person in the group will have a deviation score, even if his score is the same as the mean. In this case the deviation score will be 0 since there is no difference between the score and the mean.

For example: If the mean is 15 and John has a score of 17, his deviation score will be 17 − 15 or 2.

If the mean is 15 and Mary has a score of 15, her deviation score will be 15 − 15 or 0.

If the mean is 15 and Jim has a score of 12, his deviation score will be 12 − 15 or −3.

The minus sign indicates that Jim's score is below the mean.

Go on to frame 116c.

116c If the mean of a group of scores is 20 and if:

John has a score of 25, his deviation score is
(1) _____.

Joe has a score of 20, his deviation score is
(2) _____.

Diane has a score of 15, her deviation score is
(3) _____.

---

(1) 25 − 20 = 5

(2) $20 - 20 = 0$

(3) $15 - 20 = -5$

Go on to frame 117.

117 We represent deviation scores by the symbols $X - \overline{X}$.

So, if we have scores X_1, X_2, X_3, the deviation scores will be:

$$X_1 - \overline{X}$$
$$X_2 - \overline{X}$$
$$X_3 - \overline{X}$$

You will recall that $\overline{X}$ stands for the mean and X stands for any given score.

Go on to frame 117a.

117a Like any other scores, deviation scores can be added to find a Σ (sum of) deviation scores.

We would represent this as:

$$(X_1 - \overline{X}) + (X_2 - \overline{X}) + (X_3 - \overline{X}) + (X_4 - \overline{X}) = \Sigma(X - \overline{X}),$$

which reads, "deviation scores added together equal the sum of deviation scores."

Go on to frame 117b.

117b If we have the scores 20, 19, 18, 17, 16, 15, 14, where the mean is 17, we will have the following deviation scores:

$$20 - 17 = \underline{3}; \; 19 - 17 = \underline{2}; \; 18 - 17 = \underline{1}; \; 17 - 17 = \underline{0};$$
$$16 - 17 = \underline{-1}; \; 15 - 17 = \underline{-2}; \; 14 - 17 = -\underline{3}.$$

We can add these deviation scores to get this sum.

$$3 + 2 + 1 + 0 + (-1) + (-2) + (-3)$$

As you will remember, negative numbers can be summed just as positive numbers can.

So we have:

$$3 + 2 + 1 + 0 = 6 \text{ and}$$
$$(-1) + (-2) + (-3) = -6.$$

Therefore, the sum of the deviation scores is $6 + (-6) = 0$.

Go on to frame 117c.

117c For the following scores find $\bar{X}$, the deviation scores, and the sum of the deviation scores:

$$10, 9, 8, 7, 6, 5, 4.$$

$$\bar{X} = (1) \underline{\hspace{3em}}.$$

$(X - \bar{X}) = (2) \underline{\hspace{3em}}, \; (3) \underline{\hspace{3em}}, \; (4) \underline{\hspace{3em}}, \; (5) \underline{\hspace{3em}},$
$(6) \underline{\hspace{3em}}, \; (7) \underline{\hspace{3em}}, \; (8) \underline{\hspace{3em}}.$

$$\Sigma (X - \bar{X}) = (9) \underline{\hspace{3em}}.$$

---

(1) = 7
(2) 3, (3) 2, (4) 1, (5) 0, (6) −1, (7) −2, (8) −3,
(9) $3 + 2 + 1 + 0 + (-1) + (-2) + (-3) = 6 - 6 = 0$.

Go on to frame 117d.

117d By now you will probably have noticed that the sum of the deviation scores always equals 0. This is so since the mean is an average value and must have the same values below it as above it.

Go on to frame 118.

118 Each score, then, deviates (or differs) a given number of raw score points from the mean. We determine the extent of this deviation by finding the difference between the particular score and the mean. The sign in front of the resulting deviation indicates whether the score is <u>above</u> or <u>below</u> the mean.

How far does a score of 80 deviate from a mean of 50?
(1) _____

What would the deviation score be for a person who scored 75 in a group whose mean is 60? (2) _____

What would the deviation score be for a person who scored 35 in a group whose mean is 50? (3) _____

(1) $80 - 50 = 30$
(2) $75 - 60 = 15$
(3) $35 - 50 = -15$

Go on to frame 119.

119 In the following distribution the mean is 12:

$$20, 15, 14, 12, 10, 8, 5.$$

Each score deviates from this mean as follows:

$$20 - 12 = 8; \ 15 - 12 = 3; \ 14 - 12 = 2; \ 12 - 12 = 0;$$
$$10 - 12 = -2; \ 8 - 12 = -4; \ 5 - 12 = -7.$$

The resulting deviations are called <u>deviation scores</u>. That is, the numbers 8, 3, 2, 0, −2, −4, −7 are called deviation scores.

Find the mean and deviation scores for the following set of scores:

$$50, 40, 35, 30, 25$$

$\overline{X} = 36$
Deviation scores are: 14, 4, −1, −6, −11.
(The minus signs indicate that these scores lie below the mean.)

Go on to frame 120.

120 As you have already seen, if the scores lie below the mean, the deviation score is still found by finding the difference between each score and the mean. A minus sign is placed in front of the deviation score to indicate that the corresponding raw score is <u>below</u> the mean.

What is the deviation score for these raw scores if the mean is 45?

$$40, 42, 36, 35, 30$$

−5, −3, −9, −10, −15.

Go on to frame 121.

121 Find the deviation scores for the following raw scores. (Remember, you first have to find the mean.)

$$25, 26, 24, 30, 32, 36, 9$$

(If you are not sure you remember how to find the deviation scores, you might look at frame 117b again.)

$\overline{X} = 26$.

Deviation scores are in order of raw scores above:

$$-1, 0, -2, 4, 6, 10, -17.$$

Go on to frame 122.

122 Like any other kind of scores, deviation scores may be added to find a sum of deviations.

Example:

Raw Scores	Deviation Scores	$\overline{X} = 28$
42	14 ⎫	
36	8 ⎪	
32	4 ⎬ 28	
30	2 ⎭	
26	−2 ⎫	
25	−3 ⎪	
24	−4 ⎬ −28	
9	−19 ⎭	

Sum of deviations = (−28) + 28 = <u>0</u>.

To find the sum of the deviations you add algebraically.

Go on to frame 123.

123 Given the following set of scores:

$$40, 42, 50, 52, 57, 59, 64.$$

Find $\overline{X}$, the deviation scores for each raw score, and the sum of the deviations.

$\overline{X} = 52$

Deviation scores: $-12, -10, -2, 0, 5, 7, 12$.

Sum of deviations: $(-24) + 24 = 0$.

Go on to frame 124.

---

124 For the following set of scores, find $\overline{X}$ and indicate how far each score deviates from $\overline{X}$.

    120, 115, 112, 106, 104, 102, 100, 95, 93, 90, 85.

$\overline{X} = 102$

Deviation scores: $18, 13, 10, 4, 2, 0, -2, -7, -9, -12, -17$.

Go on to frame 125.

INTERVAL DEVIATION

125 Just as we can find deviation scores for individual raw scores, we can find deviation scores when the raw scores are arranged in frequency tables. In this case, however, we are concerned with how far, in interval units, any particular interval deviates from that in which the mean is found.

For example, $\overline{X}$ for this distribution is 72.8 and thus lies in the interval 70–74. How far do each of the other intervals deviate from this one?	85–89 3	3
	80–84 4	2
	75–79 5	1
	70–74 8	0
	65–69 6	−1
	60–64 5	−2
	55–59 4	−3

Go on to frame 125a.

125a Look at the following frequency table:

f (stands for frequency) x (stands for deviation)

105–109	7
100–104	8
95– 99	8
90– 94	10
85– 89	12
80– 84	6
75– 79	5
70– 74	4

The mean is 91.7 and therefore lies in the interval 90–94.
How far do each of the other intervals deviate from this
one? Complete the table by indicating how far each interval
deviates from the one containing the mean.

	f	x
105–109	7	3
100–104	8	2
95– 99	8	1
90– 94	10	0
85– 89	12	−1
80– 84	6	−2
75– 79	5	−3
70– 74	4	−4
$N = 60$		

Go on to frame 126.

126 Up to this point you have found the mean by summing the scores and dividing by the number of scores. When your scores are arranged in a frequency table, this is not possible, since you no longer have the individual scores.

There is a way of finding the mean from a frequency table, however. This method involves making use of the fact that we can determine how far each interval deviates from the interval in which the mean falls.

Go on to frame 127.

127 Look at the following table:

	f	
105–109	7	By looking at the frequencies we can make a good estimate as to which interval will contain the mean.
100–104	8	
95– 99	8	
90– 94	10	Let's say we choose the interval 90–94, (although we could just as well choose 85–89 or 95–99, or any other interval). Since the mean is a score, we have to choose some score within this interval. It is customary to use the
85– 89	12	
80– 84	6	
75– 79	5	
70– 74	4	
	$N = 60$	

midpoint which is $\dfrac{90 + 94}{2} = 92$.

This can be called the <u>assumed mean</u>. Our problem now is to find out how far from the actual mean we are. In other words we need to find the amount that must be either added to or subtracted from our assumed mean in order to determine the actual mean. That is, we must find the "correction factor" that is to be added to or subtracted from the assumed mean in order to give the mean.

Go on to frame 127a.

127a To find $\overline{X}$ from a frequency table we first examine the frequencies and _____ which interval will contain the mean.

estimate

Go on to frame 127b.

127b Having picked the interval in which we think the mean
lies, we then find the (1) _____ of this
interval and we call this the (2) _____
mean.

---

(1) midpoint
(2) assumed

Go on to frame 127c.

127c In order to find the mean when our scores are arranged
in a frequency table, we first examine the frequencies
and pick the interval in which we (1) _____
the mean lies. We then take the (2) _____
of this interval and call this the (3) _____
mean.

---

(1) think, estimate
(2) midpoint
(3) assumed

Go on to frame 128.

128 In the following table,

	f	x
105–109	7	4
100–104	8	3
95– 99	8	2
90– 94	10	1
85– 89	12	0
80– 84	6	−1
75– 79	5	−2
70– 74	4	−3
N =	60	

let's pick the interval 85–89 as the one in which we think the mean lies.

The assumed mean then is the midpoint of this interval or $\dfrac{85 + 89}{2} = 87$.

We have also indicated how far each other interval deviates from the interval 85–89 (which itself has a deviation of 0).

The deviations are indicated in the column headed x. The intervals below 85–89 are all preceded by a minus sign to indicate that they lie below the mean.

Go on to frame 128a.

128a Complete the following table indicating the interval which you have chosen as containing the assumed mean (it's always the midpoint of the interval) and how far from the interval containing the assumed mean each other interval deviates.

	f	x
50–54	3	
45–49	5	
40–44	8	
35–39	8	
30–34	7	
25–29	3	
20–24	2	
N =	36	

Go on to frame 129.

129 While you could have chosen any interval as the one in which the assumed mean lies, let's suppose you chose the interval 35−39. In this case the assumed mean would be $\dfrac{35 + 39}{2}$ or 37 and your frequency table would look like this:

	f	x	
50−54	3	3	These values are positive be-
45−49	5	2	cause the intervals are <u>above</u>
40−44	8	1	the mean.
35−39	8	0	
30−34	7	−1	These values are negative (−) be-
25−29	3	−2	cause the intervals are <u>below</u> the
20−24	2	−3	mean.
	$N = 36$		

Go on to frame 130.

130 Let's look at this last table again.

	f	x	fx	
50−54	3	3		Our task now is to determine how
45−49	5	2		much influence each interval
40−44	8	1		contributes to the correction
35−39	8	0		factor. That is, we have to find
30−34	7	−1		out how much each interval con-
25−29	3	−2		tributes to the assumed mean
20−24	2	−3		(A.M.) to pull it <u>up</u> to the actual
	$N = 36$			mean or <u>down</u> to the actual mean,
				as the case may be.

To find this out, we multiply the frequency (f) in each interval by its distance from the A.M. interval (x).

In other words, we multiply each f by its accompanying x.

Do so for this table and enter the results in the column fx.

Go on to frame 131.

131 The completed table from frame 130 should be:

	f	x	fx
50–54	3	3	9
45–49	5	2	10
40–44	8	1	8
35–39	8	0	0
30–34	7	−1	−7
25–29	3	−2	−6
20–24	2	−3	−6
	$N = 36$		

Now that you have found the contribution of each interval (indicated by fx), you have to find the total contribution spread over the entire table.

Go on to frame 132.

132

	f	x	fx
50–54	3	3	9
45–49	5	2	10
40–44	8	1	8
35–39	8	0	0
30–34	7	−1	−7
25–29	3	−2	−6
20–24	2	−3	−6

The fx values above the A.M. will, of course, tend to pull the A.M. up, while the fx values below the A.M. will tend to pull it down. In other words, if the total positive value is greater than the total negative value, $\overline{X}$ is going to lie above the A.M. On the other hand, if the total negative value is greater than the total positive value, $\overline{X}$ will lie below the A.M.

To find out whether the final result is one of pulling the A.M. up or down you sum all the (fx)'s above the mean and all the (fx)'s below the mean. Remember, the sum of (−) quantities is a (−) sum; i.e., $(−2) + (−3) = (−5)$. The total pull is then found by summing, algebraically, the two subtotals, that is, $\Sigma fx = (\Sigma fx \ (+)\ ) + (\Sigma fx \ (−)\ )$. For example, if the total (+) (fx)'s is 20 and the total (−) (fx)'s is $−15$ then $\Sigma fx = 20 + (−15)$ or $\underline{5}$.

Go on to frame 132a.

132a Find the *fx* for this table:

	f	*x*	*fx*
50–54	3	3	9
45–49	5	2	10
40–44	8	1	8
35–39	8	0	0
30–34	7	−1	−7
25–29	3	−2	−6
20–24	2	−3	−6
	$N = 36$		

---

	f	*x*	*fx*		
50–54	3	3	9		
45–49	5	2	10	27	$\Sigma fx = 27 + (-19) = 8.$
40–44	8	1	8		
35–39	8	0	0		
30–34	7	−1	−7		
25–29	3	−2	−6	−19	
20–24	2	−3	−6		
	$N = 36$				

What we did here, once again, was to find the sum of the positive *fx*'s and then the sum of the negative *fx*'s and add these two values together.

Go on to frame 132b.

132b Find the Σfx for the following and state what the A.M. is (the A.M. is in interval 85–89).

	f	*x*	*fx*
105–109	7		
100–104	8		
95– 99	8		
90– 94	10		
85– 89	12	0	
80– 84	6		
75– 79	5		
70– 74	4		
	$N = 60$		

Go on to frame 133.

133 The completed table should be:

	f	x	fx	
105–109	7	4	28	
100–104	8	3	24	
95– 99	8	2	16	78
90– 94	10	1	10	
85– 89	12	0	0	
80– 84	6	−1	−6	
75– 79	5	−2	−10	−28
70– 74	4	−3	−12	

The assumed mean (A.M.) is the midpoint of the interval 85–89 or 87.

$N = 60$, $\Sigma fx = 78 + (-28) = 50$.

Indicate what the A.M. of the following frequency distribution is, complete the table and find Σfx.

	f	x	fx
85–89	3		
80–84	4		
75–79	5		
70–74	8	0	
65–69	6		
60–64	5		
55–59	4		
	N = 35		

The completed table should be:

	f	x	fx	
85–89	3	3	9	
80–84	4	2	8	22
75–79	5	1	5	
70–74	8	0	0	
65–69	6	−1	−6	
60–64	5	−2	−10	−28
55–59	4	−3	−12	
	N = 35		$\Sigma fx = -6$	

The assumed mean is 72.

If your answers were correct, go on to frame 141.
If your answers were not correct, go on to frame 134.

134 While the mean can be found for <u>ungrouped</u> scores by
simply summing the scores and dividing by the number
of scores, this operation is a little more complex for
grouped or categorized scores since in this case the
<u>individual</u> scores are not available.

We find the mean from a frequency table by making use
of the fact that we can determine how far each interval
deviates from the interval in which the mean falls.

Go on to frame 135.

135 In a frequency table we can usually make a good estimate
as to which <u>interval</u> will contain the mean. Look at the
following table:

	f
105–109	7
100–104	8
95– 99	8
90– 94	10
85– 89	12
80– 84	6
75– 79	5
70– 74	4
$N = 60$	

Let's say we choose the interval 90–94. Since the mean
is a score, we have to choose some score within this interval. It is customary to use the midpoint which is
$\frac{90 + 94}{2} = 92$.

Go on to frame 136.

136 To find $\overline{X}$ from a frequency table we first examine the
frequencies and _____ which interval will
contain the mean.

---

estimate

Go on to frame 137.

137 Having picked the interval in which we think the mean lies, we then find the (1) _____ of this interval and we call this the (2) _____ mean.

_____

(1) midpoint
(2) assumed

Go on to frame 137a.

137a In order to find the mean when our scores are arranged in a frequency table we first examine the frequencies and pick the interval in which we (1) _____ the mean lies. We then take the (2) _____ of this interval and call this the (3) _____ mean.

_____

(1) think, estimate
(2) midpoint
(3) assumed

Go on to frame 138.

138

	f	x	
105–109	7	4	Let's pick the interval 85–89 as the
100–104	8	3	one in which we think the mean lies,
95– 99	8	2	although we could just as well have
90– 94	10	1	chosen 80–84 or 90–94 since we are
85– 89	12	0	just estimating which interval con-
80– 84	6	−1	tains the mean.
75– 79	5	−2	
70– 74	4	−3	The assumed mean (A.M.) then is

$N = 60$

The assumed mean (A.M.) then is the midpoint of this interval or

$$\frac{85 + 89}{2} = 87.$$

The values in the column head x indicate how far each other interval deviates from the interval 85–89. The

90

intervals below 85–89 are all preceded by a (–) sign to indicate that they lie below the mean.

Go on to frame 138a.

138a Complete the following table. Indicate the interval which you have chosen as containing the assumed mean (it's always the midpoint of the interval). Indicate, by completing the x column, how far each interval deviates from the chosen interval.

	f	x
50–54	3	
45–49	5	
40–44	8	
35–39	8	
30–34	7	
25–29	3	
2ᴜ–24	2	
$N =$	36	

You could have chosen any interval as the one in which the mean lies, but let's suppose you chose the interval 35–39. In this case the assumed mean would be $\dfrac{35 + 39}{2}$ or 37 and your frequency table would look like this:

	f	x	
50–54	3	3	These values are positive because the intervals are <u>above</u> the mean.
45–49	5	2	
40–44	8	1	
35–39	8	0	
30–34	7	−1	These values are negative because the intervals are <u>below</u> the mean.
25–29	3	−2	
20–24	2	−3	
$N =$	36		

Go on to frame 138b.

138b Look at this last table again.

	f	x	fx
50–54	3	3	
45–49	5	2	
40–44	8	1	
35–39	8	0	
30–34	7	−1	
25–29	3	−2	
20–24	2	−3	
	$N = 36$		

Your task now is to determine how much each interval contributes to the assumed mean (A.M.) to pull it up to the actual mean or down to the actual mean, as the case may be.

To find this out, the frequency (f) in each interval is multiplied by its distance from the A.M. interval (x).

In other words, you multiply each f by its accompanying x.

Do so for this table and enter the results in the column fx.

The completed table should be:

	f	x	fx
50–54	3	3	9
45–49	5	2	10
40–44	8	1	8
35–39	8	0	0
30–34	7	−1	−7
25–29	3	−2	−6
20–24	2	−3	−6
	$N = 36$		

Now that you have found the contribution of each interval to the shift of the assumed mean, you have to find the total contribution spread over the entire table.

Go on to frame 139.

139

f	x	fx
50–54	3	3	9
45–49	5	2	10
40–44	8	1	8
35–39	8	0	0
30–34	7	−1	−7
25–29	3	−2	−6
20–24	2	−3	−6

$N = 36$

The fx values <u>above</u> the A.M. will, of course, tend to pull the A.M. up, while the fx values <u>below</u> the A.M. will tend to pull it down.

To find out whether the final result pulls the A.M. up or down you sum all the fx's above the mean and all the fx's below the mean. (Remember, the sum of negative quantities is a negative sum; i.e., $(-2) + (-3) = -5$.) The total pull is then found by summing, algebraically, the two subtotals.

In other words; $\Sigma fx = (\Sigma fx\ (+)) + (\Sigma fx\ (-))$. For example, if the total (+) fxs is 20 and the total (−) fxs is −15, then $\Sigma fx = 20 + (-15)$ or <u>5</u>.

Now find the Σfx for this table.

Go on to frame 140.

140

f	x	fx
50–54	3	3	9
45–49	5	2	10
40–44	8	1	8
35–39	8	0	0
30–34	7	−1	−7
25–29	3	−2	−6
20–24	2	−3	−6

$N = 36$

27

−19

$\Sigma fx = 27 + (-19) = 8$.

What we did here, once again, was to find the sum of the positive fx's and then the sum of the negative fx's and add these two values together.

Go on to frame 141.

93

141 Given the following frequency table, complete the table and find Σfx. Take 106–108 as the interval containing the assumed mean. (Indicate what the A.M. is.)

	f
115–117	2
112–114	2
109–111	4
106–108	6
103–105	3
100–102	2
97– 99	1
	$N = 20$

Go on to frame 142.

142 The completed table from the last frame should be:

	f	x	fx		
115–117	2	3	6 ⎤		
112–114	2	2	4 ⎬	14	A.M. $= \dfrac{106 + 108}{2} = 107$.
109–111	4	1	4 ⎦		
106–108	6	0	0		
103–105	3	−1	−3 ⎤		
100–102	2	−2	−4 ⎬	−10	
97– 99	1	−3	−3 ⎦		
	$N = 20$		$\Sigma fx = 4$		

Find Σfx for the following table. Take 42–47 as the interval containing the A.M. (Indicate what the A.M. is.)

	f
60–65	2
54–59	2
48–53	3
42–47	6
36–41	7
30–35	4
24–29	2
18–23	1
$N = 27$	

$\Sigma fx = -12;$ A.M. = 44.5

Go on to frame 143.

CORRECTION FACTORS

143 You will recall that in order to find $\overline{X}$ using the A.M. it is necessary to find a correction factor which must then be either added to the A.M. or subtracted from it.

The Σfx is the basis of this correction factor. To complete the correction we need two modifications:

(1) Since we want to correct for a mean, the correction must be a mean correction so we divide Σfx by N.

(2) Since the correction is going to be some part of an interval, or some multiple of an interval, we must multiply by i (the size of the interval).

Therefore, the complete correction factor is $\left(\dfrac{\Sigma fx}{N}\right) i.$

Go on to frame 144.

144 To complete the correction factor for the mean you must modify Σfx.

The first modification is to find the "mean correction." To find this we divide Σfx by (1) _____.

The second modification is to find how much of an interval the correction is. To find this we multiply the result of the first modification by (2) _____.

The complete correction factor then is (3) _____.

---

(1) N

(2) i (interval size)

(3) $\left(\dfrac{\Sigma fx}{N}\right) i$

If your answers are correct, go on to frame 147.
If your answers are not correct, go on to frame 145.

145 To find $\overline{X}$ using the A.M. it is first necessary to find a correction factor which must then be either added to the A.M. or subtracted from it.

The basis of this correction factor is Σfx. To complete the correction we need two modifications:

(1) Since we want to correct for a mean, the correction we need is a mean or average correction, so we divide Σfx by N, the number of persons in our sample.

(2) Since the correction is going to be either some part of an interval, or some multiple of an interval, we must multiply by i (the size of the interval).

Therefore, the complete correction factor is the Σfx divided by N and multiplied by i; i.e., $\left(\dfrac{\Sigma fx}{N}\right) i$.

Go on to frame 146.

146 To complete the correction factor for the mean we must modify Σfx.

The first modification is to find the "mean correction." To find this we divide Σfx by (1) _____ .

The second modification is to find how much of an interval the correction is. To find this we multiply the result of the first modification by (2) _____ .

The complete correction factor then is (3) $\left(\dfrac{\Sigma fx}{\rule{1cm}{0.4pt}} \right)$ _____ .

---

(1) N

(2) i (interval size)

(3) $\left(\dfrac{\Sigma fx}{N} \right) i$

Go on to frame 147.

FINDING THE MEAN FROM FREQUENCY TABLES

147 For the following table, take the interval 130–134 as that containing the A.M. Indicate what the A.M. would be, complete the table, then find the Σfx and the complete correction factor.

	f	x	fx
145–149	2		
140–144	2		
135–139	4		
130–134	6	0	
125–129	3		
120–124	1		
115–119	2		
	$N = 20$		

(If you wish you may review frames 142, 143, 144, and 145 again before starting this question.)

97

	f	x	fx	
145–149	2	3	6 ⎫	
140–144	2	2	4 ⎬ 14	
135–139	4	1	4 ⎭	
130–134	6	0	0	
125–129	3	−1	−3 ⎫	
120–124	1	−2	−2 ⎬ −11	
115–119	2	−3	−6 ⎭	

$N = 20 \qquad \Sigma fx = 14 - 11 = \underline{3}.$

$$\text{A.M.} = \frac{130 + 134}{2} = 132$$

$$\text{Correction factor} = \left(\frac{\Sigma fx}{N}\right)i = \frac{3}{20} \cdot 5 = .75$$

Go on to frame 148.

148 Find Σfx for the following table. Take 104–107 as the interval containing the A.M. What is the A.M.? Complete the correction factor.

	f
120–123	2
116–119	3
112–115	3
108–111	4
104–107	6
100–103	3
96– 99	1
92– 95	2
$N =$	

Go on to frame 149.

149 The complete table from frame 148 should be:

	f	x	fx		
120–123	2	4	8		Now you are ready to find
116–119	3	3	9	27	$\bar{X}$. To find $\bar{X}$, add (alge-
112–115	3	2	6		braically) the correction
108–111	4	1	4		factor to the A.M.
104–107	6	0	0		
100–103	3	−1	−3		
96– 99	1	−2	−2	−11	Find $\bar{X}$ in this case.
92– 95	2	−3	−6		
	$N = 24$		$\Sigma fx = 16$		

$$\text{A.M.} = \frac{104 + 107}{2} = 105.5$$

$$\text{Correction factor} = \left(\frac{16}{24}\right) 4 = 2.67$$

$$\bar{X} = \text{A.M.} + \left(\frac{\Sigma fx}{N}\right) i$$

$$= 105.5 + 2.67 = 108.17$$

Go on to frame 150.

150 To find the mean of a distribution from a frequency table you take an (1) _____ _____ and then find the necessary (2) _____ _____. This is found by using the formula: $\bar{X} = \text{A.M.} + (3)$ _____.

---

(1) assumed mean
(2) correction factor

(3) $\bar{X} = \text{A.M.} + \left(\dfrac{\Sigma fx}{N}\right) i$

Go on to frame 151.

151 Find $\bar{X}$ of the following distribution taking 51–53 as the interval containing the A.M.

	f	x	fx
60–62	2		
57–59	3		
54–56	3		
51–53	4	0	0
48–50	4		
45–47	2		
42–44	1		

$$N = \underline{\hspace{2cm}} \qquad \Sigma fx = \underline{\hspace{2cm}}$$

$$\text{A.M.} = \underline{\hspace{1.5cm}}$$

$$\text{Correction factor} = \left(\frac{\Sigma fx}{?}\right) \; ? = \underline{\hspace{2cm}}$$

$$\bar{X} = \underline{\hspace{1.5cm}}$$

$N = 19$

$\Sigma fx = 15 - 11 = 4$

$$\text{Correction factor} = \frac{4}{19} \cdot 3 = .63$$

A.M. $= 52$

$\bar{X} = 52 + .63 = \underline{52.63}$

Go on to frame 152.

152 Find $\overline{X}$ for this distribution taking 68−71 as the interval containing the A.M.

	f
80−83	1
76−79	3
72−75	2
68−71	5
64−67	4
60−63	3
56−59	2

$N =$ _____

A.M. = _____

Correction factor = _____

$\overline{X} =$ _____

$N = 20$

$\Sigma fx = 11 - 16 = -5$

Correction factor $= \dfrac{-5}{20} \cdot 4 = -1$

A.M. $= \dfrac{68 + 71}{2} = 69.5$ (The midpoint of the interval 68−71.)

$\overline{X} = 69.5 + (-1) = 69.5 - 1 = 68.5$

Go on to frame 152a.

152a Find $\overline{X}$ for this distribution, using any interval you wish as that containing the A.M.

	f
50−53	1
46−49	1
42−45	2
38−41	4
34−37	6
30−33	3
26−29	2
22−25	1

No matter what A.M. you chose, $\overline{X}$ should work out to be 36.5.

Go on to frame 153.

153 To find $\overline{X}$ for a distribution from a frequency table you first take an _____ _____.

assumed mean

Go on to frame 154.

154 The second step is to find how much each interval
(1) _____ from that containing the A.M. This is entered in the column headed (2) _____.

(1) deviates
(2) x

Go on to frame 155.

155 The third step is to find how much each interval contributes to the pull, either up or down, on the A.M. To find this you multiply the (1) _____ column by the (2) _____ column.

102

(1) f
(2) x

Go on to frame 156.

156 The fourth step is to find the _____ of the fx column.

_____

sum

Go on to frame 157.

157 The fifth step is to find the **necessary correction factor.**
To find this correction **factor you divide** Σfx **by**
(1) _____ and multiply by (2) _____ .

_____

(1) N
(2) i (interval size)

Go on to frame 158.

158 The final step in finding $\bar{X}$ is to (1) _____ the
(2) _____ _____ to the
(3) _____ .

_____

(1) add
(2) correction factor
(3) A.M.

Go on to frame 159.

159 Find the mean of the following distribution:

	f
110–114	5
105–109	4
100–104	7
95– 99	9
90– 94	15
85– 89	4
80– 84	3
75– 79	3

$\overline{X} = 95.6$

Go on to frame 160.

160 Find the mode and the median of the following set of scores:

99, 98, 98, 97, 94, 89, 88, 87, 87, 87, 86, 84, 84, 83, 80, 80, 80, 80, 79, 76, 73, 72, 72, 71, 70, 69.

---

mode = 80
median = 83.5

If your answers are correct, go on to frame 166.
If your answers are not correct, go on to frame 161.

161 One way to find the median is to rank order the scores and simply find the midpoint of the rank-ordered set of scores. For example:

11, 10, 9, 7, 6, 5, 3, 2, 1.

These scores are rank ordered. There are eleven scores so the halfway point would be the fifth score or the score 6.

Rank order the following scores and find the median:

24, 23, 25, 27, 30, 21, 18, 17, 22, 26, 14, 15, 16.

When we rank order the scores we get:

30, 27, 26, 25, 24, 23, 22, 21, 18, 17, 16, 15, 14.

Counting halfway up the set of scores we find the score 22 to be the midscore or the median.

Go on to frame 161a.

161a Find the median of the following set of scores:

45, 46, 50, 40, 42, 39, 51, 49, 47, 48, 37, 35, 52, 53, 38.

When the scores are rank ordered we get:

53, 52, 51, 50, 49, 48, 47, 46, 45, 42, 40, 39, 38, 37, 35.

The halfway point in this distribution is the score 46. The median therefore is 46.

Go on to frame 162.

162 54, 48, 50, 52, 51, 44, 47, 46, 39, 43, 41, 42, 35, 38, 37.

The median of the above set of scores is (1) _____ . It is the median because it is the (2) _____ score.

---

(1) 44
(2) middle or midpoint

Go on to frame 163.

163 So far we have looked only at distributions with odd numbers of scores (13 scores, 15 scores, etc.). If the distribution has an even number of scores (for example, 16 scores), the median is still halfway through the distribution, but now it is a point rather than a score.

In this case, the median is found by finding the point midway between the middle 2 scores of the distribution.

Go on to frame 164.

164 Look at this set of scores:

$$15, 14, 13, 12, 10, 9, 7, 6, 5, 4.$$

Since there is an even number of scores, the median must lie midway between the middle 2 scores. In this distribution the middle 2 scores are 10 and 9. The point halfway between them is $\dfrac{10 + 9}{2}$ or 9.5. 9.5 is, therefore, the median of the above distribution.

Find the median for this distribution. (Remember, you have to rank order the scores first.)

$$20, 21, 18, 17, 23, 16, 15, 24, 27, 26.$$

Since there is an even number of scores, the median will lie halfway between the middle 2 scores which are 21 and 20. The median, therefore, is $\dfrac{21 + 20}{2}$ or 20.5.

Go on to frame 165.

165 Find the median of the following set of scores:

$$97, 87, 94, 90, 86, 87, 88, 93, 82, 85, 95,$$
$$92, 81, 80, 98, 99.$$

89

Since there is an even number of scores (14), the median lies midway between the 2 middle scores (which are 88 and 90). Therefore, the median is $\dfrac{88 + 90}{2} = 89$.

Go on to frame 165a.

165a The mode is the most frequent score. Find the mode of the following set of scores:

$$15, 14, 14, 12, 10, 10, 10, 8, 5.$$

10

Go on to frame 166.

166 Now set up a frequency table for these scores and find $\overline{X}$ from the frequency table. (Use 5 as the interval size and start your table with the score 66.)

99, 98, 98, 97, 94, 89, 88, 87, 87, 87, 86, 84, 84,
83, 80, 80, 80, 80, 79, 76, 73, 72, 72, 71, 70, 69.

---

	f
96–100	4
91– 95	1
86– 90	6
81– 85	3
76– 80	6
71– 75	4
66– 70	2
$N =$	26
$\overline{X} =$	83

If your answer is correct, go on to frame 176.
If your answer is not correct, go on to frame 167.

167 Examine the following table:

	f	x	fx
50−54	3	3	
45−49	5	2	
40−44	8	1	
35−39	8	0	
30−34	7	−1	
25−29	3	−2	
20−24	2	−3	
$N = 36$			

Your task is to determine how much influence each interval exerts on the correction factor. That is, you have to find out how much each interval contributes to the assumed mean (A.M.) to pull it up to the actual mean, or down to the actual mean, as the case may be.

To find this out, you multiply the frequency (f) in each interval by its distance from the A.M. interval (x).

In other words, you multiply each (f) by its accompanying x.

Do so for this table and enter the results in the column fx.

Go on to frame 168.

168 The completed table from frame 167 should be:

	f	x	fx
50−54	3	3	9
45−49	5	2	10
40−44	8	1	8
35−39	8	0	0
30−34	7	−1	−7
25−29	3	−2	−6
20−24	2	−3	−6
$N = 36$			

Now that you have found the contribution of each interval, you have to find the total contribution spread over the entire table.

Go on to frame 169.

169

	f	x	fx
50—54	3	3	9
45—49	5	2	10
40—44	8	1	8
35—39	8	0	0
30—34	7	−1	−7
25—29	3	−2	−6
20—24	2	−3	−6
	$N = 36$		

The fx values above the A.M. will, of course, tend to pull the A.M. up, while the fx values below the A.M. will tend to pull it down.

To find out whether the final result is one of pulling the A.M. up or down you sum all the fx's above the mean and all the fx's below the mean. Remember the sum of negative quantities is a negative sum; i.e., $(−2) + (−3) = (−5)$. The total pull is then found by summing, algebraically, the two subtotals.

In other words: $\Sigma fx = (\Sigma fx \ (+)) + (\Sigma fx \ (−))$. For example, if the total positive fx's is 20 and the total negative fx's is −15 then $\Sigma fx = 20 + (−15)$ or 5.

Now find the Σfx for this table.

Go on to frame 170.

170

	f	x	fx	
50–54	3	3	9	
45–49	5	2	10	27
40–44	8	1	8	
35–39	8	0	0	
30–34	7	−1	−7	
25–29	3	−2	−6	−19
20–24	2	−3	−6	
$N = 36$				

$\Sigma fx = 27 + (-19) = 8.$

What we did here, once again, was to find the sum of the positive fx's and then the sum of the negative fx's and add these two values together.

Find Σfx for the following and state what the A.M. is. (The A.M. is in interval 85–89.)

	f	x	fx
105–109	7		
100–104	8		
95– 99	8		
90– 94	10		
85– 89	12	0	
80– 84	6		
75– 79	5		
70– 74	4		
$N = 60$			

Go on to frame 171.

171 The completed table should be:

	f	x	fx	
105–109	7	4	28	
100–104	8	3	24	
95– 99	8	2	16	78
90– 94	10	1	10	
85– 89	12	0	0	
80– 84	6	−1	−6	
75– 79	5	−2	−10	−28
70– 74	4	−3	−12	
$N = 60$			$\Sigma fx = 78 + (-28) = \underline{50}$	

The assumed mean (A.M.) is the midpoint of the interval 85–89 or $\underline{87}$.

Go on to frame 172.

CORRECTION FACTOR MODIFICATIONS

172 You will recall that in order to find $\overline{X}$ using the A.M. it is necessary to find a correction factor which must then be either added to the A.M. or subtracted from it. The basis of this correction factor is Σfx. To complete the correction we need two modifications:

(1) The correction must be a mean correction so we divide Σfx by N.

(2) Multiply the correction by i (the size of the interval).

Therefore, the complete correction factor is $\left(\dfrac{\Sigma fx}{N}\right)i$.

Go on to frame 173.

173 Complete the x and the fx column for the following table. Take 104–107 as the interval containing the A.M. Indicate what the A.M. is, and find Σfx and the correction factor.

	f	x	fx
120–123	2		
116–119	3		
112–115	3		
108–111	4		
104–107	6		
100–103	3		
96– 99	1		
92– 95	2		
$N =$			

Go on to frame 173a.

173a The complete table from frame 173 should be:

	f	x	fx		
120–123	2	4	8		
116–119	3	3	9	27	Now you are ready to find $\overline{X}$. To find $\overline{X}$, add (alge-
112–115	3	2	6		braically) the correction
108–111	4	1	4		factor to the A.M.
104–107	6	0	0		
100–103	3	−1	−3		
96– 99	1	−2	−2	−11	Find $\overline{X}$ in this case.
92– 95	2	−3	−6		
$N = 24$			$\Sigma fx = 16$		

$$\text{A.M.} = \frac{104 + 107}{2} = 105.5$$

$$\text{Correction factor} = \frac{16}{24} \cdot 4 = 2.67$$

$$\overline{X} = \text{A.M.} + \frac{\Sigma fx}{N} \, i$$

$$= 105.5 + 2.67 = 108.17$$

Go on to frame 174.

174 To find the mean of a distribution from a frequency table
you take an (1) _____ _____ and
then find the necessary (2) _____
_____ which is found by using the formula:

$$\overline{X} = \text{A.M.} + (3) \underline{\quad\quad}.$$

---

(1) assumed mean

(2) correction factor

(3) $\overline{X} = \text{A.M.} + \left(\dfrac{\Sigma fx}{N}\right)i.$

Go on to frame 175.

175 Now set up a frequency table for these scores and find $\overline{X}$
from the frequency table. (Use an interval size of 5 and
start your table with the score 100.)

99, 98, 98, 97, 94, 89, 88, 87, 87, 87, 86, 84, 84,
83, 80, 80, 80, 80, 79, 76, 73, 72, 72, 71, 70, 69.

---

	f
96–100	4
91– 95	1
86– 90	6
81– 85	3
76– 80	6
71– 75	4
66– 70	2

$$N = 26$$

$$\overline{X} = 83$$

Go on to frame 175a.

Spread, Dispersion, or Variability

175a The mean, as you have seen, is one way to describe a group. However, its value is limited since it only expresses the most expected or representative score within the group. In order to evaluate more completely any group of scores it is necessary to have some expression of the <u>spread</u> of scores within that group.

Go on to frame 176.

176 Another of the things we frequently want to do when discussing groups of people is to compare two groups.

One way of comparing groups is to use the <u>mean</u> performance. However, as you know, the mean doesn't tell us anything about the <u>spread</u> of the scores in each group.

Two groups may have the same mean, but one group could have most of its scores very close to the mean while the other could have its scores widely spread out. In other words, one group may be quite homogeneous while the other group may be quite heterogeneous.

Go on to frame 177.

177 In order to get a more complete description of a group or a truer comparison of two groups, then, we should examine not only their means but also the _____ of scores in the group or groups.

This characteristic of distributions of scores is commonly referred to as <u>variability</u>.

---

spread

Go on to frame 178.

RANGE

178 One way to express the spread, dispersion or variability of
scores in a group of scores is by the range of scores.

By range of scores we mean the distance between the
highest and lowest score in the group.

Go on to frame 179.

179 The distance between the highest and lowest scores,
called the (1) _____ , is a very crude measure of
the spread or (2) _____ or
_____ of a group of scores.

(1) range
(2) dispersion or variability

Go on to frame 179a.

179a The range of the following scores:

25, 24, 23, 20, 18, 15, 14, 11, 10, 9, 8.

is _____ .

$25 - 8 = 17$

Go on to frame 180.

DEVIATION SCORES

180 Another way of expressing the dispersion or variability of
scores is in terms of their deviations from the mean; that
is, the differences between each score and the mean.

When we say a score deviates from the mean we mean that
it is _____ from the mean.

different

Go on to frame 181.

181 In statistical shorthand, we express the deviation of a score from the mean $(\bar{X})$ as $X - \bar{X}$ where X stands for a raw score and $\bar{X}$ for the mean.

For example, if we wanted to express the fact that we were dealing with the deviations of, say, three raw scores we would do so by:

$$X_1 - \bar{X}; X_2 - \bar{X}; X_3 - \bar{X}$$

where X_1 stands for the first score, X_2 for the second score and X_3 for the third score.

Find the deviations for the following scores when the mean is 25.

28, 30, 35, 20, 15.

$28 - 25 = \quad 3$
$30 - 25 = \quad 5$
$35 - 25 = \quad 10$
$20 - 25 = \quad -5$
$15 - 25 = -10$

Go on to frame 182.

182 Each of these deviations is called a deviation score.

For example, the deviation scores for the following raw scores, when the mean is 70, are:

Raw Score	Deviation Score
80	$80 - 70 = 10$
75	$75 - 70 = \quad 5$
70	$70 - 70 = \quad 0$
65	$65 - 70 = -5$
62	$62 - 70 = -8$

Find the deviation scores for the following raw scores when the mean is 35.

$$38, 35, 30, 28, 25, 50, 60, 40.$$

$38 - 35 = 3$	$25 - 35 = -10$
$35 - 35 = 0$	$50 - 35 = 15$
$30 - 35 = -5$	$60 - 35 = 25$
$28 - 35 = -7$	$40 - 35 = 5$

Go on to frame 182a.

182a Deviation scores are scores which express the
(1) _____ between the mean and a
(2) _____ _____ .

---

(1) difference
(2) raw score

Go on to frame 183.

183 Find the deviation scores for the following raw scores when the mean is 40. (Remember, the deviation score is found by: $X_1 - \overline{X}; X_2 - \overline{X}; X_3 - \overline{X}$.)

$$35, 30, 38, 40, 51, 48, 40, 47, 46, 55.$$

$-5, -10, -2, 0, 11, 8, 0, 7, 6, 15$

Go on to frame 183a.

183a Find the deviation scores for the following raw scores. (Remember, before you can find the deviation scores you have to know the (1) _____ .) $\overline{X} =$ (2) _____ .

$$30, 31, 38, 42, 40, 58, 50, 55, 54, 51, 43.$$

(If you have forgotten how to find the deviation scores, you might review frames 119 and 120 again.)

---

(1) mean
(2) 44.7

Deviation scores: $30 - 44.7 = -14.7$; $31 - 44.7 = 13.7$; $38 - 44.7 = -6.7$; $42 - 44.7 = -2.7$; $40 - 44.7 = -4.7$; $58 - 44.7 = 13.3$; $50 - 44.7 = 5.3$; $55 - 44.7 = 10.3$; $54 - 44.7 = 9.3$; $51 - 44.7 = 6.3$; $43 - 44.7 = -1.7$.

Go on to frame 184.

184 Find the deviation scores for the following raw scores:

100, 101, 99, 90, 110, 115, 95, 100, 92, 90, 95, 105.

$\overline{X} = 99.3$

Deviation scores: .7; 1.7; −.3; −9.3; 10.7; 15.7; −4.3; .7; −7.3; −9.3; −4.3; 5.7.

Go on to frame 185.

AVERAGE DEVIATION

185 We can find a sum (Σ) of deviation scores and a mean ($\overline{X}$) of deviation scores, just as we can for any other kind of scores.

To find the Σ of any scores we (1) _____ the scores.

To find $\overline{X}$ we (2) _____ the Σ of the scores by the (3) _____ of scores.

---

(1) add
(2) divide
(3) number (N)

Go on to frame 186.

186 Find the sum of the deviation scores, <u>ignoring the alge-braic sign</u>, for the following set of raw scores. That is,

add the deviation scores ignoring whether they are (positive) or (negative).

80, 85, 79, 77, 79, 82, 84, 88, 78, 91, 85.

$\overline{X}$ = 82.5 (rounded off to 1 decimal place)

Σ of deviation scores = 2.5 + 2.5 + 3.5 + 5.5 + 3.5 + .5 + 1.5 + 5.5 + 4.5 + 8.5 + 2.5 = 40.5.

Go on to frame 187.

187 For the following raw scores find the Σ of the deviation scores, ignoring the algebraic sign. Find $\overline{X}$ for the deviation scores:

15, 25, 22, 24, 30, 35, 38, 34, 34, 36.

$\overline{X}$ for raw scores = 29.3

Σ of deviation scores = 14.3 + 4.3 + 7.3 + 5.3 + 0.7 + 5.7 + 8.7 + 4.7 + 4.7 + 6.7 = 62.4.

$\overline{X}$ of the deviation score = $\dfrac{62.4}{10}$ = 6.24 (without regard to algebraic sign).

Go on to frame 188.

188 The mean of a set of deviation scores (without regard to algebraic sign) is called the average deviation.

The average deviation is the _____ of a set of deviation scores, without regard to algebraic sign.

---

mean

Go on to frame 189.

189 Like the range, the average deviation is a measure of the _____ of a group of scores.

___

spread or dispersion

Go on to frame 190.

190 Find the average deviation of the following set of scores:

125, 130, 131, 127, 116, 132, 118, 117, 115, 122, 126, 127.

___

$\overline{X}$ = 123.8
average deviation = 5.2

Go on to frame 191.

191 Find $\overline{X}$ and the average deviation for the following distribution of scores:

30, 31, 38, 42, 40, 58, 50, 55, 54, 51, 43.

(Remember, the average deviation is the mean of the deviation ignoring the sign.)

___

$\overline{X}$ = 44.7

average deviation = 8.1 (rounded off to one decimal)

Go on to frame 192.

192 The way in which the mean of a set of scores and the average deviation of the same set of scores differ is:

The mean is the arithmetic average of the
(1) _____ scores while the average deviation is the arithmetic average of the (2) _____ scores without regard to algebraic sign.

___

(1) raw
(2) deviation

Go on to frame 193.

193 Find $\overline{X}$ and the average deviation of the following set of scores:

35, 30, 38, 40, 51, 48, 40, 47, 46, 55.

$\overline{X} = 43.0$

average deviation = 6.4

Go on to frame 194.

194 A point made earlier was that for the purposes of comparing two groups, knowing just the mean of the groups is not enough. It is also necessary to know something about the way the scores in each group are spread out. That is, we must have information about the dispersion of scores in each group.

Let's take a look at why knowing the dispersion of scores within each group is so important.

Go on to frame 194a.

194a Here is a graphical representation of the distribution of scores in three groups all having the <u>same</u> mean.

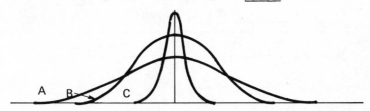

Since the means of these three distributions are the same, what is different about the distributions?

Think about this question a bit before going on to the next frame.

Go on to frame 195.

195 The thing that is different about these three groups is the dispersion or spread of the scores. In other words, the scores in group A are more spread out than those in groups B or C; and the scores in group B are more spread out than those in group C.

Go on to frame 196.

STANDARD DEVIATION

196 You've already seen that we can describe this dispersion by means of either the range or the average deviation.

Another, and better way, is in terms of what is known as the standard deviation of the scores.

Go on to frame 197.

197 Let's review the average deviation for a moment.

The average deviation is the (1) _____ of the deviation scores. To find it we (2) _____ all the deviation scores and then (3) _____ by the (4) _____ of such scores.

(1) mean or average
(2) add
(3) divide
(4) number

Go on to frame 198.

198 The standard deviation (which we represent by the symbol σ) can be found in a way that is somewhat similar to finding the average deviation.

Go on to frame 199.

199 To find the standard deviation (σ) for ungrouped scores, we use the deviation scores just as in the case of the average deviation. In this case, however, we use the <u>squared</u> deviation scores.

The way we find the standard deviation (σ) for ungrouped scores is to take the <u>square root</u> of the mean of the squared deviation scores.

Expressed in symbols this is:

$$\sigma = \sqrt{\frac{\Sigma (X - \overline{X})^2}{N}} \, .$$

Go on to frame 200.

200 To find the standard deviation of ungrouped scores we use the formula:

$$\sigma = \sqrt{\frac{\Sigma (X - \bar{X})^2}{N}}.$$

For example, the σ of these scores:

25, 26, 26, 28, 30, 31, 35, 35, 38, 40, 42, 43, 43, 48, 50

is $\bar{X} = 36$.

The squared deviation scores would be:

$(25 - 36)^2 = 11^2 = 121$
$(26 - 36)^2 = 10^2 = 100$
100
64
36
25

$1 \qquad \dfrac{\Sigma (X - \bar{X})^2}{N} = \dfrac{958}{15} = 63.9$
1
4
16
$36 \qquad \sigma = \sqrt{\dfrac{\Sigma (X - \bar{X})^2}{N}} = \sqrt{63.9} = 7.99$
49
49
144
196
$\Sigma (X - \bar{X})^2 = \overline{958}$

Go on to frame 200a.

200a In other words, to find the standard deviation of un-grouped scores using the formula

$$\sigma = \sqrt{\frac{\Sigma (X - \bar{X})^2}{N}}$$

we first find the deviation score corresponding to each raw score $(X - \bar{X})$, square each of these deviation scores $(X - \bar{X})^2$, and then find the sum of (total) all these squared deviation scores; $\Sigma (X - \bar{X})^2$. Having found the sum of the squared deviation scores we divide by the number of scores (N)

$$\frac{\Sigma(X - \bar{X})^2}{N}$$

and then we find the square root of the resulting number

$$\sqrt{\frac{\Sigma(X - \bar{X})^2}{N}} \; .$$

Go on to frame 200b.

200b Find the standard deviation of a set of scores:

15, 16, 17, 18, 19, 20, 21, 22, 23, 24.

(1) First, find $\bar{X}$ = _____ .

(2) Then, find the deviation scores: $15 - 19.5 = -4.5$
$16 - 19.5 = -3.5$

$24 - 19.5 = 4.5$

(3) Square each of the deviation scores: $(-4.5)^2 = 20.3$
$(-3.5)^2 = 12.3$

$(4.5)^2 = 20.3$

(4) Find the sum of the squared deviation scores.

$20.3 + 12.3 + \ldots + 20.3 =$ _____ .

(5) Divide by $N = \dfrac{81.0}{10} =$ _____ .

(6) Find the square root (use a table or long-hand method).

$\sqrt{8.1} =$ _____ . This is the standard deviation.

Complete this exercise.

(1) 19.5
(2) −4.5; −3.5; −2.5; −.5; .5; 2.5; 3.5; 4.5.
(3) 20.3; 12.3; 6.3; 2.3; .3; .3; 2.3; 6.3; 12.3; 20.3.
(4) 81.0
(5) 8.1
(6) 2.8

Go on to frame 200c.

200c Find the standard deviation for the following set of scores using the formula $\sigma = \sqrt{\dfrac{\Sigma(X - \bar{X})^2}{N}}$:

$$11, 11, 12, 14, 15, 15, 15, 18,$$
$$19, 21, 22, 24, 24, 25, 26, 28$$

(Round off your deviation scores and squared deviations to one decimal; e.g., 5.41 = 5.4; 5.45 = 5.5.)

$\bar{X} = 18.8$

$\Sigma(X - \bar{X})^2 = 479.04$

$\dfrac{\Sigma(X - \bar{X})^2}{N} = \dfrac{479.04}{16} = 29.94$

$\sigma = \sqrt{\dfrac{\Sigma(X - \bar{X})^2}{N}} = \sqrt{29.94} = 5.5$

If your answer is correct, go on to frame 206.
If your answer is not correct, go on to frame 201.

201 Let's review the average deviation again.

The average deviation is the (1) _____ of the deviation scores. To find it we (2) _____ all the deviation scores and then (3) _____ by the (4) _____ of such scores.

---

(1) mean or average
(2) add

(3) divide

(4) number

Go on to frame 202.

202 To find the standard deviation we use deviation scores also. In this case though, we use the <u>squares</u> of the deviation scores. In other words, we <u>square</u> each of the deviation scores and use these squared scores.

For example, suppose we had the following scores:

$$5, 6, 7, 8, 9, 10, 11, 12.$$

$\overline{X} = 8.5$

For average deviation we would use $(X - \overline{X})$:	For standard deviation we would use $(X - \overline{X})^2$:
$5 - 8.5 = 3.5$	$(5 - 8.5)^2 = (3.5)^2 = 12.3$
$6 - 8.5 = 2.5$	$(6 - 8.5)^2 = (2.5)^2 = 6.3$
$7 - 8.5 = 1.5$	$(7 - 8.5)^2 = (1.5)^2 = 2.3$
$8 - 8.5 = .5$	$(8 - 8.5)^2 = (.5)^2 = .3$
$9 - 8.5 = .5$	$(9 - 8.5)^2 = (.5)^2 = .3$
$10 - 8.5 = 1.5$	$(10 - 8.5)^2 = (1.5)^2 = 2.3$
$11 - 8.5 = 2.5$	$(11 - 8.5)^2 = (2.5)^2 = 6.3$
$12 - 8.5 = 3.5$	$(12 - 8.5)^2 = (3.5)^2 = \underline{12.3}$
$\Sigma(X - \overline{X}) = 16.0$	$\Sigma(X - \overline{X})^2 = 42.4$

Go on to frame 203.

203 Having squared each of the deviation scores $[(X - \bar{X})^2]$ we add up these squares $[\Sigma (X - \bar{X})^2]$ and divide by the number of scores $\left[\dfrac{\Sigma (X - \bar{X})^2}{N}\right]$.

The standard deviation is the square root of this last expression. That is,

$$\sigma = \sqrt{\frac{\Sigma (X - \bar{X})^2}{N}} .$$

For example, using the scores from frame 202:

$$\Sigma (X - \bar{X})^2 = 42.4$$

$$\frac{\Sigma (X - \bar{X})^2}{N} = \frac{42.4}{8} = 5.3$$

$$\sigma = \sqrt{\frac{\Sigma (X - \bar{X})^2}{N}} = \sqrt{5.3} = 2.3$$

Go on to frame 204.

204 To find the standard deviation of ungrouped scores we use the formula:

$$\sigma = \sqrt{\frac{\Sigma (X - \bar{X})^2}{N}} .$$

For example, let's find σ for these scores:

25, 26, 26, 28, 30, 31, 35, 35, 38, 40, 42, 43, 43, 48, 50 with $\bar{X} = 36$.

The squared deviation scores would be:

$(25 - 36)^2 = 11^2 = 121$
$(26 - 36)^2 = 10^2 = 100$
100
64
36
25 $\dfrac{\Sigma(X - \overline{X})^2}{N} = \dfrac{958}{15} = 63.9$
1
1
4
16 $\sigma = \sqrt{\dfrac{\Sigma(X - \overline{X})^2}{N}} = \sqrt{63.9} = 7.99$
36
49
49
144
196
$\Sigma(X - \overline{X})^2 = \overline{958}$

Go on to frame 204a.

204a Find the standard deviation for the following set of scores using the formula

$$\sigma = \sqrt{\frac{\Sigma(X - \overline{X})^2}{N}}$$

51, 51, 52, 54, 55, 55, 55, 58, 59, 61, 62, 64, 64, 65, 66, 68

(Round off your deviation scores and squared deviations to one decimal; e.g., 5.41 = 5.4; 5.45 = 5.5.)

$\overline{X} = 58.8$

$\Sigma(X - \overline{X})^2 = 479.04$

$\dfrac{\Sigma(X - \overline{X})^2}{N} = \dfrac{479.04}{16} = 29.94$

$\sigma = \sqrt{\dfrac{\Sigma(X - \overline{X})^2}{N}} = \sqrt{29.94} = 5.47 = 5.5.$

Go on to frame 205.

205 Find σ for the following set of scores:

32, 9, 15, 32, 31, 40, 8, 31, 12, 18, 6, 22, 16, 12, 15.

(You may, if you wish, look at frames 202 and 203 again before doing this exercise.)

$\overline{X} = 19.9$

$\Sigma (X - \overline{X})^2 = 1592.9$

$\dfrac{\Sigma (X - \overline{X})^2}{N} = 106.19$

$\sigma = \sqrt{\dfrac{\Sigma (X - \overline{X})^2}{N}} = \sqrt{106.19} = 10.3$

Go on to frame 205a.

205a Another simpler formula for the calculation of the standard deviation for ungrouped data which can be derived from

$$\sqrt{\dfrac{\Sigma (X - \overline{X})^2}{N}} \text{ is } \sigma = \sqrt{\dfrac{\Sigma X^2}{N} - \overline{X}^2}$$

Go on to frame 205b.

205b To calculate σ by the formula $\sigma = \sqrt{\dfrac{\Sigma X^2}{N} - \overline{X}^2}$ you sum the squares of the original scores, divide this sum by N, subtract the value of the mean squared and take the square root.

Using the scores from frame 204a, calculate σ by means of this formula: $\overline{X} = 58.8$.

Sum the squares of all the scores: $(51)^2 + (51)^2 + (52)^2 + \ldots + (68)^2 = \Sigma X^2$.

$$\Sigma X^2 = 2601 + 2601 + 2704 + \ldots + 4624 = 55{,}803$$

$$\frac{\Sigma X^2}{N} = \frac{55{,}803}{16} = 3487.7$$

$$\frac{\Sigma X^2}{N} - \overline{X}^2 = 3487.7 - 3457.4 = 30.3$$

$$\sqrt{30.3} = 5.5 = \sigma$$

Go on to frame 206.

206 Before going on, let's review what has been covered so far regarding measures of dispersion.

The three measures of dispersion are:

(1) _____ ; (2) _____
_____ ; (3) _____
_____ .

---

(1) range
(2) average deviation
(3) standard deviation

Go on to frame 207.

207 The range is the (1) _____ between the
(2) _____ and (3) _____ scores.

The average deviation is the (4) _____ of
the (5) _____ scores.

The standard deviation is the square root of the
(6) _____ of the deviation scores squared.

---

(1) difference
(2) highest
(3) lowest
(4) average
(5) deviation
(6) mean

Go on to frame 208.

STANDARD DEVIATION FOR GROUPED SCORES

208 So far, we've looked at how we go about finding the standard deviation for ungrouped scores. Now, let's look at how the standard deviation is found for <u>grouped</u> scores.

Go on to frame 209.

209 You will recall that the frequency table set up for calculating the mean had four columns:

<u>Interval</u> f x fx

To calculate the standard deviation we have to add one more column: fx^2 $(x \cdot fx = fx^2)$.

The complete table, then, looks like this:

<u>Interval</u> f x fx fx^2

Go on to frame 210.

210 The formula by which the standard deviation is calculated from grouped data is:

$$\sigma = i\sqrt{\frac{\Sigma fx^2}{N} - \left(\frac{\Sigma fx}{N}\right)^2}$$

where $\left(\dfrac{\Sigma fx}{N}\right)^2$ is a correction factor just as $\dfrac{\Sigma fx}{N}$ is when calculating the mean, and where i is the interval size.

Go on to frame 211.

211 To calculate the standard deviation for grouped scores we proceed as follows:

	f	x	fx	fx^2	
50–54	3	3	9	$(3 \cdot 9) = 27$	$\sigma = i\sqrt{\dfrac{\Sigma fx^2}{N} - \left(\dfrac{\Sigma fx}{N}\right)^2}$
45–49	5	2	10	$(2 \cdot 10) = 20$	
40–44	8	1	8	$(1 \cdot 8) = 8$	$= 5\sqrt{\dfrac{92}{36} - \left(\dfrac{8}{36}\right)^2}$
35–39	8	0	0	0	
30–34	7	−1	−7	$(-1 \cdot -7) = 7$	$= 5\sqrt{2.56 - (.22)^2}$
25–29	3	−2	−6	$(-2 \cdot -6) = 12$	
20–24	2	−3	−6	$(-3 \cdot -6) = 18$	$= 5\sqrt{2.56 - .05}$
	$N = 36$		$\Sigma fx^2 = 8$	$\Sigma fx^2 = 92$	$= 5\sqrt{2.51}$
	$i = 5$				$= 5 \cdot 1.58$
					$\sigma = 7.90$

Go on to frame 212.

133

212 Complete the following frequency table and calculate the standard deviation. Before starting you may look at frame 211 again, if you wish.

	f	x	fx	fx^2
105–109	7			
100–104	8			
95– 99	8			
90– 94	10			
85– 89	12	0	0	0
80– 84	6			
75– 79	5			
70– 74	4	—	—	—

$$N = 60 \qquad \Sigma fx = \qquad \Sigma fx^2 = \qquad i =$$

$$\sigma = i\sqrt{\frac{\Sigma fx^2}{N} - \left(\frac{\Sigma fx}{N}\right)^2}$$

(Remember, fill in the formula correctly.)

$\Sigma fx = \ 50$

$\Sigma fx^2 = 288$

$$\sigma = 5\sqrt{\frac{288}{60} - \left(\frac{50}{60}\right)^2}$$

$\sigma = 5\ \sqrt{4.11}$

$\sigma = 5 \cdot 2.03$

$\sigma = 10.2$

Go on to frame 213.

213 Set up the appropriate frequency table and calculate the standard deviation for the following scores. Start with the score 66 and use interval size of 5.

99, 98, 98, 97, 94, 89, 88, 87, 87, 87, 86, 84, 84, 83, 80, 80, 80, 80, 79, 76, 73, 72, 72, 71, 70, 69.

---

	f	x	fx	fx^2
96–100	4	4	16	64
91– 95	1	3	3	9
86– 90	6	2	12	24
81– 85	3	1	3	3
76– 80	6	0	0	0
71– 75	4	−1	−4	4
66– 70	2	−2	−4	8

$N = 26 \quad \Sigma fx = 26 \quad \Sigma fx^2 = 112$

$$\sigma = i\sqrt{\frac{\Sigma fx^2}{N} - \left(\frac{\Sigma fx}{N}\right)^2}$$

$$= 5\sqrt{\frac{112}{26} - \left(\frac{26}{26}\right)^2}$$

$$= 5\sqrt{4.31 - 1}$$

$$= 5\sqrt{3.31}$$

$$= 5 \cdot 1.82$$

$$\sigma = 9.1$$

If your answer is correct, go on to frame 218.
If your answer is not correct, go on to frame 214.

214 The frequency table set up for calculating the mean had four columns:

Interval f x fx

To calculate the standard deviation we have to add one more column: fx^2 which is obtained by finding $x \cdot fx = fx^2$.

The complete table, then, looks like this:

Interval f x fx fx^2
          (table)
$N =$ $\Sigma fx =$ $\Sigma fx^2 =$

Go on to frame 215.

215 The formula by which the standard deviation is calculated from grouped data is:

$$\sigma = i\sqrt{\frac{\Sigma fx^2}{N} - \left(\frac{\Sigma fx}{N}\right)^2} \ .$$

where $\left(\dfrac{\Sigma fx}{N}\right)^2$ is a correction factor just as $\dfrac{\Sigma fx}{N}$ is when calculating the mean and where i is the interval size.

Go on to frame 216.

135

216 To calculate the standard deviation for grouped scores we proceed as follows:

	f	x	fx	fx^2	
50–54	3	3	9	$(3 \cdot 9) = 27$	
45–49	5	2	10	$(2 \cdot 10) = 20$	
40–44	8	1	8	$(1 \cdot 8) = 8$	
35–39	8	0	0	0	
30–34	7	−1	−7	$(-1 \cdot -7) = 7$	
25–29	3	−2	−6	$(-2 \cdot -6) = 12$	
20–24	2	−3	−6	$(-3 \cdot -6) = 18$	

$$\sigma = i\sqrt{\frac{\Sigma fx^2}{N} - \left(\frac{\Sigma fx}{N}\right)^2}$$

$i = 5 \quad N = 36 \quad \Sigma fx = 8 \quad \Sigma fx^2 = 92 \qquad \frac{\Sigma fx}{N} = \frac{8}{36} \qquad \frac{\Sigma fx^2}{N} = \frac{92}{36}$

$$\sigma = 5\sqrt{\frac{92}{36} - \left(\frac{8}{36}\right)^2}$$

$$= 5 \sqrt{2.56 - (.22)^2}$$

$$= 5 \sqrt{2.56 - .05}$$

$$= 5 \sqrt{2.51}$$

$$= 5 \cdot 1.58$$

$$\sigma = 7.90$$

Go on to frame 217.

217 Set up the appropriate frequency table and calculate the standard deviation for the following scores. Start with the score 66 and use an interval size of 5.

99, 98, 98, 97, 94, 89, 88, 87, 87, 87, 86, 84, 84, 83, 80, 80, 80, 80, 79, 76, 73, 72, 72, 71, 70, 69.

	f	x	fx	fx^2
96–100	4	4	16	64
91– 95	1	3	3	9
86– 90	6	2	12	24
81– 85	3	1	3	3
76– 80	6	0	0	0
71– 75	4	−1	−4	4
66– 70	2	−2	−4	8

$$N = 26 \quad \Sigma fx = 26 \quad \Sigma fx^2 = 112$$

$$i = 5 \quad \frac{\Sigma fx}{N} = \frac{26}{26} \quad \frac{\Sigma fx^2}{N} = \frac{112}{26}$$

$$\sigma = i\sqrt{\frac{\Sigma fx^2}{N} - \left(\frac{\Sigma fx}{N}\right)^2}$$

$$= 5\sqrt{\frac{112}{26} - \left(\frac{26}{26}\right)^2}$$

$$= 5\sqrt{4.31 - 1}$$

$$= 5\sqrt{3.31}$$

$$= 5 \cdot 1.82$$

$$\sigma = 9.1$$

Go on to frame 218.

218 Calculate the mean and standard deviation for the following set of scores. Start your frequency table with the interval 115–119 and use an interval size of 5.

116, 117, 120, 126, 127, 129, 130, 130, 131, 132, 132, 134, 136, 137, 137, 138, 141, 143, 145, 148.

---

	f	x	fx	fx^2
145–149	2	3	6	18
140–144	2	2	4	8
135–139	4	1	4	4
130–134	6	0	0	0
125–129	3	−1	−3	3
120–124	1	−2	−2	4
115–119	2	−3	−6	18

$$N = 20 \quad \Sigma fx = 3 \quad \Sigma fx^2 = 55$$

A.M. = 132

$$\sigma = 5\sqrt{2.73} = 5 \cdot 1.65$$

$$\overline{X} = 132 + 5\left(\frac{3}{20}\right) = 132.75$$

$$\sigma = 8.25 = 8.3$$

$$\sigma = i\sqrt{\frac{\Sigma fx^2}{N} - \left(\frac{\Sigma fx}{N}\right)^2} = 5\sqrt{\frac{55}{20} - \left(\frac{3}{20}\right)^2}$$

Go on to frame 219.

137

219 One of the basic purposes of descriptive statistics is to help us meaningfully order and interpret test scores.

You have already examined several ways in which this can be accomplished: frequency distributions, measures of central value, deviation scores and standard deviation are all techniques for helping us order and interpret test scores.

Go on to frame 220.

220 Frequency distributions impose order.

Means and medians help endow meaning through an expression of central or average value.

Standard deviations lend meaning through an expression of the extent of the spread of scores.

Deviation scores are meaningful because they express distance from the mean value.

Go on to frame 221.

Transformed Scores

221 Deviation scores are an example of a <u>transformation</u>. That is, the original score has been <u>transformed</u> to another kind of expression of performance.

Expressions of performance are transformed from one system to another (e.g., when we transform raw scores to deviation scores) because this transformation helps us to more meaningfully express this performance in relation to some standard. (In the case of deviation scores performance is being expressed in relation to mean performance for a group.)

Go on to frame 222.

222 Transforming scores has the effect of systematically altering certain characteristics of a set of scores but not others.

For example, when a set of raw scores is <u>transformed</u> to deviation scores the <u>mean</u>, as you know, becomes <u>zero</u>. However, all the other characteristics such as variability, the shape of the distribution and the rank order of the scores remain unchanged.

Other transformations effect changes in the mean and the standard deviation of the set of scores but leave the shape of the distribution unchanged. Still other transformations change not only the mean and standard deviation but also the shape of the distribution.

Go on to frame 223.

z SCORES

223 As you can see, there are a number of kinds of transformations each yielding its own system of <u>transformed</u> <u>scores</u>.

One such transformation yields what is known as a <u>standard score</u> or <u>z score</u>.

Go on to frame 224.

224 You will recall that we can transform raw scores to deviation scores $(X - \bar{X})$. If we take this deviation score $(X - \bar{X})$ and divide it by the standard deviation we get a new score, a <u>standard score</u> or <u>z score</u>.

Go on to frame 225.

225 Raw scores are frequently transformed to z scores because z scores have several advantageous properties:

1. First, z scores express performance in terms of the individual's position relative to the mean and standard deviation of a given group of scores.

2. Also, z scores for the same individual over several samples of performance are directly comparable. This is not always possible with raw scores because of differences in test units. Transforming to z scores expresses performance from all samples in terms of standard deviation units.

Go on to frame 226.

226 The formula for finding a standard score or z score is:

$$z = \frac{X - \bar{X}}{\sigma}$$

Go on to frame 227.

227 We can change raw scores into _____ or
_____ scores by dividing the deviation score $(X - \overline{X})$
by the standard deviation.

---

standard or z

Go on to frame 228.

228 A standard or z score is obtained from the
_____ score by dividing the
_____ score by the _____
_____.

---

deviation
deviation
standard deviation

Go on to frame 229.

229 *Example:* To find standard scores, given the raw scores in frame 204a:

51, 51, 52, 54, 55, 55, 58, 59, 61, 62, 64, 64, 65, 66, 68

we first find the mean $(\overline{X}) = 58.8$.

The standard deviation is $\sigma = 5.5$.

Deviation Scores	Divided by σ		Standard or z Scores
$51 - 58.8 = -7.8$	5.5	=	-1.4
$51 - 58.8 = -7.8$	5.5	=	-1.4
$52 - 58.8 = -6.8$	5.5	=	-1.2
$54 - 58.8 = -4.8$	5.5	=	$-.9$
$55 - 58.8 = -3.8$	5.5	=	$-.7$
$55 - 58.8 = -3.8$	5.5	=	$-.7$
$58 - 58.8 = -0.8$	5.5	=	$-.01$
$59 - 58.8 = 0.2$	5.5	=	$.004$
$61 - 58.8 = 2.2$	5.5	=	$.4$
$62 - 58.8 = 3.2$	5.5	=	$.6$
$64 - 58.8 = 5.2$	5.5	=	$.9$
$64 - 58.8 = 5.2$	5.5	=	$.9$
$65 - 58.8 = 6.2$	5.5	=	1.1
$66 - 58.8 = 7.2$	5.5	=	1.3
$68 - 58.8 = 9.2$	5.5	=	1.7

As you see, some of the z scores are negative values and others are positive. The reason for this is that some of the scores lie below the mean (51, 52, 54, 55, 58) while others fall above it (59, 61, 62, 64, 65, 66, 68). Therefore, their respective standard scores have either negative or positive values.

Go on to frame 230.

230 Calculate the standard or z scores for the following raw scores for which the mean is 20 and the standard deviation is 10:

32, 9, 15, 32, 31, 40, 8, 31, 12, 18, 6, 22, 16, 12, 15.

(You may look at frame 229 again before starting, if you wish.)

Deviation scores:
12, −11, −5, 12, 11, 20, −12, 11, −8, −2, −14, 2, −4, −8, −5.

z scores (deviation scores divided by σ):
1.2, −1.1, −.5, 1.2, 1.1, 2.0, −1.2, 1.1, −.8, −.2, −1.4, .2, −.4, −.8, −.5.

Go on to frame 231.

231 Calculate the z scores for the following raw scores:

99, 98, 98, 97, 94, 89, 88, 87, 87, 87, 86, 84, 84, 83, 80, 80, 80, 80, 79, 76, 73, 72, 72, 71, 70, 69.

(If you are not sure of the procedure, look at frame 222 again.)

(Remember, you first have to find the mean and standard deviation.)

$\overline{X}$ = 83.2   (If you are within .3 or .4 of these values, this
σ = 9.1   is close enough.)

z scores = 15.8, 14.8, 14.8, 13.8, 10.8, 5.8, 4.8, 3.8, 3.8, 3.8, 2.8, .8, .8, −.2, −3.2, −3.2, −3.2, −3.2, −4.2, −7.2, −10.2, −11.2, −11.2, −12.2, −13.2, −14.2.

Go on to frame 232.

143

Z SCORES

232 By this time you will have noted one of the disadvantages of z scores; namely, they very frequently involve the use of decimals and minus signs. This is not always convenient. In order to avoid decimals and negative values, z scores are frequently changed to Z scores.

Since Z scores are simply another way of expressing performance in terms of standard measure they possess the same properties as z scores.

Go on to frame 233.

233 Thus, z scores are changed to Z scores in order to avoid the need to deal with minus signs and decimals.

The formula for z scores is: $z = \dfrac{X - \bar{X}}{\sigma}$.

To get rid of the decimals we multiply the z values by a constant and get:

$$\left(\frac{X - \bar{X}}{\sigma}\right)10 \quad \text{(Commonly 10 is the constant used.)}$$

To get rid of the minus signs we <u>add</u> some constant (large enough to assure that all values will be positive) to the above formula and get:

$$50 + \left(\frac{X - \bar{X}}{\sigma}\right) \quad \text{(Commonly 50 is the constant used.)}$$

Go on to frame 234.

234 Thus, Z scores are found by multiplying z values by a constant and then adding a constant to each resulting value.

$$Z = 50 + \left(\frac{X - \bar{X}}{\sigma}\right) 10$$

Go on to frame 235.

235 Using 50 and 10 as your constants complete the following formula:

$$Z = \underline{\hspace{1cm}} + \left(\frac{X - \bar{X}}{\sigma}\right) \underline{\hspace{1cm}}.$$

$$Z = 50 + \left(\frac{X - \bar{X}}{\sigma}\right) 10$$

Go on to frame 236.

236 Use the raw scores in frame 229 to find the Z scores corresponding to each raw score.

$51 + 50 + (-1.4)\ 10 = 36$		$55 = 50 + (-.7)\ \ 10 = 43$		$64 = 59$
$51 =$	36	$55 =$	43	$64 = 59$
$52 =$	38	$58 = 50 + (-.01)\ 10 = 49.9$		$65 = 61$
$54 =$	41	$59 =$	49.9	$66 = 63$
		$61 = 50 + (.4)\ \ \ 10 = 54$		$68 = 67$
		$62 =$	56	

Go on to frame 237.

237 Using the raw scores in frame 230 find the Z scores corresponding to each raw score.

z scores	Z scores	z scores	Z scores
1.2	62	− .2	48
−1.1	39	−1.4	36
− .5	45	.2	52
1.2	62	− .4	46
1.1	61	− .8	42
2.0	70	− .5	45
−1.2	38		
− .8	42		

Go on to frame 238.

PERCENTILES

238 Changing a group of scores from their raw score value
to percentiles or percentile points is another transformation which allows expression of an individual's score with
reference to his group. In this case the score is expressed
as a rank order proportion of the group.

Go on to frame 239.

239 You will remember that the median is that score below
which 50% of the group of scores fall. The median is,
therefore, the 50th percentile or P_{50}. In other words the
50th percentile is that score below which 50% of the
scores fall and above which 50% of the scores fall.
Similarly, that score below which 70% of the scores fall
and above which 30% fall is the 70th percentile or P_{70}.

Go on to frame 239a.

239a Complete the following:

The score below which 65% of scores and above which 35%
fall is the (1) _____.

The score below which 35% of scores fall and above which
65% fall is the (2) _____.

146

The score below which 45% of scores fall and above which 55% fall is the (3) _____.

---

(1) 65th percentile
(2) 35th percentile
(3) 45th percentile

Go on to frame 239b.

239b That score below which 25% of scores fall and above which 75% fall is known as the _____.

25th percentile

Go on to frame 239c.

239c In other words, percentiles express for any given percentile that proportion of the group of scores which fall below the given percentile value and that proportion which fall above it.

Go on to frame 240.

240 As you will recall, by convention any score X has upper and lower limits of $X - (.5)$ and $X + (.5)$. In other words, a given score, say 15, really occupies the interval 14.5 − 15.5, with the value 15 being merely the midpoint of this interval.

You should bear this fact in mind as you go through the following frames.

Go on to frame 241.

241 Given the following group of scores find P_{30}.

10, 25, 23, 24, 19, 18, 20, 15, 17, 13, 14, 12.

First rank order the scores:

1	2	3	4	5	6	7	8	9	10	11	12
10,	12,	13,	14,	15,	17,	18,	19,	20,	23,	24,	25.

For this group N is 12.

We want that score below which 30% of the scores fall so we first find 30% of 12 which, of course, is 4 (3.6). In other words, 4 scores will fall below P_{30}. The 4th score is 14, the upper limit of which is 14.5. This is the point below which 30% of the group fall and above which 70% fall and is, therefore, P_{30}.

Go on to frame 241a.

241a Given the following scores find P_{40}. (Fill in the blanks.)

25, 26, 27, 28, 29, 30, 31, 32, 33, 34, 35,
36, 37, 38, 39, 40, 41, 42, 43, 44, 45.

$N = (1)$ _____

We want the score below which (2) _____ % of the scores fall.

(3) _____ % of (4) _____ = (5) _____

The (6) _____th score is (7) _____. The upper limit of this score is (8) _____ and, therefore, P_{40} is (9) _____.

---

(1) 21	(4) 21	(7) 32
(2) 40%	(5) 8 (8.4 rounded)	(8) 32.5
(3) 40%	(6) 8th	(9) 32.5

Go on to frame 242.

148

242 Find the 60th percentile for the following group of scores:

31, 32, 33, 34, 35, 36, 37, 38, 39, 40, 41, 42,
43, 44, 45, 46, 47, 48, 49, 50, 51, 52.

$P_{60} = 43.5$

$N = 22$; 60% of 22 = 13. The 13th score is 43 and the upper limit of this score is 43.5. Since this is the score below which 60% of the scores fall it must be the 60th percentile.

Go on to frame 243.

243 Find the 55th percentile point for the following group of scores:

41, 42, 43, 44, 45, 46, 47, 48, 49, 50, 51, 52,
53, 54, 55, 56, 57, 58, 59, 60, 61, 62, 63.

$N = 23$ 55% = 13   13th score = 53 $P_{55} = 53.5$

Go on to frame 244.

244 Now examine the case where we have tie scores and want to find a given percentile point.

Assume we want the 45th percentile point in the following group of scores:

20, 21, 22, 23, 24, 26, 28, 30, 30, 30, 30, 30, 38, 40, 41, 42, 44, 45, 47, 50.

Recall that we want that point <u>below</u> which 45% of these scores fall. For this group of scores N is 20 and 45% of 20 is 9, so we want that point below which the first 9 scores fall. However, in this case the 9th score is 30 and five individuals have a score of 30. That is, five individuals have scores within the limits 29.5 − 30.5. Since 7 of the required 9 scores fall below 29 we obviously need 2 of the 5 scores in the interval 29.5 − 30.5. Therefore, we must interpolate $\frac{2}{5}$ of the way up this interval or .4. Since the interval size is 1, .4 is the value which must be added to the lower limit of our interval or 29.5. Thus the point below which 9 scores fall is 29.5 + .4 or 29.9. Therefore, 29.9 is the 45th percentile point.

Read this frame over several times.

Go on to frame 245.

245 Find the 55th percentile point in the following group of scores:

31, 32, 33, 34, 35, 36, 37, 37, 37, 39, 40, 41, 42, 44, 46.

Work through this example and fill in the blanks.

N = 15; 55% of 15 = (1) _____ . We want the score below which (2) _____ individuals fall. The required score is (3) _____ . However, we note that (4) _____ scores occupy the interval (5) _____ − _____ . We need (6) _____ of these (7) _____ scores; therefore, we must interpolate (8) _____ of the way up this interval. Since the interval size is one, (9) _____ is (10) _____ . We, therefore, add (11) _____ to the lower limit of the interval. P_{55}, therefore, is (12) _____.

---

(1) 8 (8.25 rounded) (5) $36.5 - 37.5$
(2) 8 (6) 2 (9) $\frac{2}{3}$
(3) 37 (7) 3 (10) .66 or .7
(4) 3 (8) $\frac{2}{3}$ (11) .7
  (12) 37.2

Go on to frame 246.

246 Given the following group of scores find the 45th percentile.

> 60, 61, 62, 63, 64, 65, 66, 67, 67,
> 67, 67, 68, 69, 70, 71, 72, 73.

$P_{45} = 66.8$

Since N is 17 and 45% of 17 is 8 we want the point below which the lower eight scores fall. The eighth score is 67, but there are four such scores. Since the seventh score is 66 we need only one of these four scores. We, therefore, interpolate $\frac{1}{4}$ of the way into the interval $66.5 - 67.5$, which is .25. We then add .25 to the lower limits of our interval and get 66.8.

Go on to frame 247.

247 Find the 55th percentile given the following group of scores:

> 22, 23, 25, 26, 27, 28, 29, 30, 31, 32, 33,
> 33, 33, 34, 35, 36, 37, 38, 39, 40, 41.

$P_{55} = 33.2$

Go on to frame 248.

Correlation Coefficient

248 So far, we have examined how a single group of scores can be treated to derive meaning from them. Now we will go one step further and examine one of the ways in which we can derive meaning from more than one group of scores on the same group of persons.

Frequently in everyday life we see instances where things are related. For example, the price of a house is related to the demand for houses. When there is a greater demand, the price goes up; when there is a lesser demand, the price comes down. Another example is that tall people typically tend to weigh more than short people with the tallest tending to weigh the most and the shortest to weigh the least.

Go on to frame 249.

249 Assume that we have two sets of scores on a group of students. One set is from an English test and the other set is from a French test. One of the questions frequently asked in this situation is: "Is there a relationship between these two groups of scores such that those persons who did best on the English test tend also to have done best on the French test?" In other words, do high grades in English tend to be <u>associated</u> with high grades in French?

When we ask such questions we are really asking if there is a <u>relationship</u> between the observed variables.

Go on to frame 250.

250 Suppose two tests are given to a group of students—an English vocabulary test and a reading comprehension test. One of the observations one might want to make could be: "What is the relationship between performance on the vocabulary test and performance on the reading test?" One of the techniques for describing this kind of relationship is <u>correlation</u>.

<u>Correlation</u> is a measure of relationship between two or more variables. The degree of this relationship is expressed by the <u>correlation coefficient</u> represented by the symbol "r."

Go on to frame 251.

251 The size of the correlation coefficient, r, expresses the degree of a relationship and may range from +1 through 0 to -1. That is, the maximum size r may reach is 1. Zero indicates no relationship.

Go on to frame 252.

252 Let's look again at our vocabulary and reading tests. If those who scored the highest on one scored the highest on the other, and if those who scored second on one scored second on the other and so on, we would have a <u>perfect positive</u> relationship which would be indicated by $r = +1$.

If, on the other hand, those who did <u>best</u> on the first test did <u>worst</u> on the second, and those who did second best on the first test did second worst on the other test and so on, we would have a perfect negative relationship which would be indicated by $r = -1$.

Finally, if performance on one test was in <u>no way</u> related to performance on the other, r would equal 0.

Go on to frame 253.

253 As you can see we may have varying degrees of relationship with r assuming values of such magnitude as 1, .9, .8, .73, 0, $-.25$, $-.42$, $-.95$, -1 and all values in between these.

Go on to frame 254.

254 Complete the following statements:

Correlation is a (1) _____ of
(2) _____ between two variables.

The degree of the relationship is expressed by the
(3) _____ _____ represented
by the symbol (4) _____.

The magnitude of the correlation between variables may
range from (5) _____ through (6) _____ to (7) _____.

(1) measure   (4) r (7) -1
(2) relationship   (5) $+1$
(3) correlation coefficient   (6) 0

Go on to frame 255.

255 The correlations we described can be illustrated by:

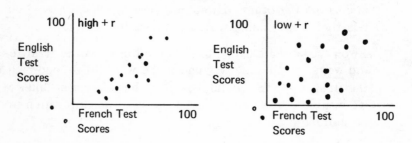

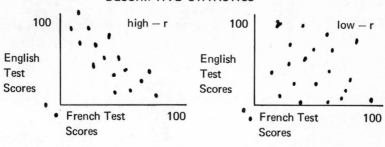

DESCRIPTIVE STATISTICS

Go on to frame 256.

256 One of the ways in which r may be calculated is by means of the formula:

$$r_{ab} = \frac{\Sigma\, xy}{\sqrt{(\Sigma\, x^2)\,(\Sigma\, y^2)}}$$

where r_{ab} = correlation coefficient derived from tests A and B.

x = deviation score on one test.

y = deviation score on the second test.

x^2 = deviation score squared.

y^2 = deviation score squared.

Go on to frame 257.

257 Find the correlation between the following sets of scores.
(Note the manner in which the table is set up.)

Indi-viduals	Scores on Test A X	Scores on Test B Y	x	y	xy	x^2	y^2
A	15	14	+4.5	+3.5	15.85	20.25	12.25
B	14	13	+3.5	+2.5	8.75	12.25	6.25
C	13	15	+2.5	+4.5	11.35	6.25	20.25
D	12	10	+1.5	−0.5	−0.75	2.25	0.25
E	11	12	+0.5	+1.5	0.75	0.25	2.25
F	10	11	−0.5	+0.5	−0.25	0.25	0.25
G	9	9	−1.5	−1.5	2.25	2.25	2.25
H	8	7	−2.5	−3.5	8.75	6.25	12.25
I	7	8	−3.5	−2.5	8.75	12.25	6.25
J	6	6	−4.5	−4.5	20.25	20.25	20.25

$$\Sigma X = 105 \quad \Sigma Y = 105 \quad \Sigma xy = 82.55 \quad \Sigma x^2 = 825.0$$

$$\bar{X} = 10.5 \quad \bar{Y} = 10.5 \quad \Sigma y^2 = 825.0$$

$$r_{ab} = \frac{\Sigma xy}{\sqrt{(\Sigma x^2)(\Sigma y^2)}}$$

$$= \frac{82.55}{\sqrt{(825)(825)}}$$

$$= \frac{82.55}{825}$$

$$r_{ab} = 0.10$$

Go on to frame 258.

258 Find the correlation between the following sets of scores.
(Complete the table and fill in the blanks.)

Indi-vidual	Scores on Test A X	Scores on Test B Y	x	y	xy	x^2	y^2
A	25	30	8.1	12.1	98.01	65.61	146.41
B	22	20	5.1	2.1			
C	20	25					
D	18	24					
E	17	20					
F	16	15					
G	15	12					
H	14	14					
I	12	10					
J	10	9	−6.9	−8.9	___	___	___

$\Sigma X =$ _____ $\Sigma Y =$ _____ $\Sigma xy =$ _____

$\bar{X} =$ _____ $\bar{Y} =$ _____ $\Sigma x^2 =$ _____

$\Sigma y^2 =$ _____

$$r_{ab} = \frac{\Sigma xy}{\sqrt{(\quad)(\quad)}} = \frac{}{\sqrt{}}$$

$r_{ab} =$ _____

$\Sigma X = 169$ $\Sigma Y = 179$ $\Sigma xy = 258.12$

$\bar{X} = 16.9$ $\bar{Y} = 17.9$ $\Sigma x^2 = 184.48$

$\Sigma y^2 = 442.90$

$$r_{ab} = \frac{258.12}{\sqrt{81706.192}} = \frac{258.12}{285.70}$$

$r_{ab} = 0.90$

Go on to frame 259.

259 Find the correlation between the following sets of scores:

Individual	Scores on Test A X	Scores on Test B Y
A	26	5
B	24	8
C	22	6
D	20	10
E	18	12
F	16	20
G	14	14
H	12	16
I	10	17
J	8	18

$\Sigma X = 170 \qquad \Sigma Y = 126 \qquad \Sigma xy = -250$

$\bar{X} = 17.0 \qquad \bar{Y} = 12.6 \qquad \Sigma x^2 = 330.0$

$$\Sigma y^2 = 246.4$$

$$r_{ab} = \frac{-250.00}{285.17} = -0.88$$

Go on to frame 260.

260 There are, of course, other ways in which to calculate r and as you proceed further in statistics you will undoubtedly encounter a number of these.

GOOD LUCK!

WORK SPACE

WORK SPACE

WORK SPACE

WORK SPACE

WORK SPACE

WORK SPACE

Use this portion
of the page to
mask the answers.

Appleton-Century-Crofts
NEW YORK | DIVISION OF MEREDITH CORPORATION